CW01080699

Another Icarus

Percy Pilcher and the Quest for Flight

Philip Jarrett

SMITHSONIAN INSTITUTION PRESS
WASHINGTON, D.C. LONDON

This book was edited by Venka V. Macintyre

Library of Congress Cataloging-in-Publication Data

Jarrett, Philip.
Another Icarus.

Bibliography: p.
Includes index.
1. Pilcher, Percy. 2. Aeronautics—Great Britain—
Biography. 3. Aeronautics—Great Britain—History.
I. Title.
TL540.P5155J37 1987 629.13′ 0092′ 4 [B] 86-17761
ISBN 0-87474-556-X (alk. paper)

The paper used in this publication meets the minimum
requirements of the American National Standard for Perma-
nence of Paper for Printed Library Materials Z39.48–1984.

COVER ILLUSTRATION: *Percy Pilcher in the Hawk on top of the "Knob" at Eynsford, 1897. (Smithsonian Institution)*

FRONTISPIECE: *A portrait of Percy Sinclair Pilcher (1867–99), taken about 1895–96. (Author)*

Contents

To Percy Pilcher

Youthful dreams of flight, nurtured in your heart,
Matured as you matured; became a part
Of ev'ry waking day.
And pensive hours on landlost, windswept seas,
Where graceful, long-winged seabirds soared with ease,
Helped guide you on your way.

Then came the day you built your fledgling wings
Of bamboo, wire, and fabric—fragile things
On which life would rely.
A pilgrimage to Berlin followed now,
Where Master Lilienthal showed you how
To trespass in the sky.

In pioneering steps the work progressed,
Bat, clumsy Beetle, Gull, and then the best;
The light and sturdy Hawk.
Towed aloft by gently plodding horses
To vie with Nature's sly and unseen forces:
An airborne, bobbing cork.

Tough yet athletic, soon you learned the way
To hold control within your body's sway
And make the sky your own.
To longer flights your airy dreams then soared,
And with the help of businessman and lord
Your new machine was grown.

But ere the test of powered wings began,
A hasty, ill-timed flight upset the plan
To which you'd given birth.
Death's evil sirens did your soul entice
To make the last and greatest sacrifice;
Then cast you to the earth.

How great a game of chance, how close to fame,
Yet few are those who now recall your name
Or what your courage meant.
The lonely grave in Brompton where you lie
Grows mossy underneath a mocking sky:
A short life bravely spent.

But those who now traverse the lofty ways
In these jet-powered, ocean-spanning days
Cast hist'ry in their wake.
You knew this time would come, and played your part
In teaching Man a new and wond'rous art:
And gave life for its sake.

Philip Jarrett
April 19, 1983

To my father, the late W. H. Jarrett, who suffered his son's obsession with airplanes when he'd already had enough of them in the war.

To the four air-minded men who fostered my youthful enthusiasm, and whose selfless encouragement set me on course: R. Glyn Davies, headmaster of Gearies Secondary Modern School for Boys; Flt. Lt. Sydney R. Barber of 4F (Ilford) Squadron, Air Training Corps; John W. R. Taylor, aviation writer; and Jack Beaumont, pilot and doyen of aviation booksellers.

Preface

"Percy's immortality is in your hands." This sobering statement by ninety-year-old Thora Forrester, Percy Pilcher's niece and the last surviving person to have known him, suddenly brought home the responsibility of my undertaking. Thora died in January 1983, when this manuscript was barely begun, but her words remained with me as I worked.

Thora's uncle was a leading aviation pioneer, yet he is little known, even to the great majority of those interested in the subject. What little has hitherto been written about him is full of inaccuracies, misinterpretations and unfounded speculation. As the first Briton to die for the cause of powered flight, and only the second person in the world to do so, Pilcher deserved better. Yet in a way it was his own fault that history allowed such a sacrifice to be forgotten, to become cloaked in obscurity. So involved was he in the pursuit of his goal that he found no time to set down a continuing record of his work.

Unlike his famous successors, the Wright Brothers, Pilcher concentrated on practical flight trials almost to the exclusion of mathematical theory and scientific experiment. We have no systematic performance estimates, aerodynamic tables and calculations, or even a diary or flight log. Moreover, he was a reluctant correspondent, seldom wrote at length when he did take up a pen, and apparently kept no letters. Therefore, to piece together the story of the five years he spent experimenting with hang gliders and the influences upon his work, one has to delve into private and public archives, search contemporary literature, and trace descendants. No one could have been more surprised than I to see the completeness of the finished account.

It is a story of single-mindedness, determination in the face of ridicule, and courage. It also provides insight into aviation's early history, particularly in Britain, and into some of the leading players in the story. In those distant days, powered, heavier-than-air flight was generally regarded as the pursuit of eccentrics and fools. The few perceptive men who did see something of its enormous potential looked to one another for mutual support and encouragement.

As Pilcher realized, there was an enormous amount to be learned—more than any one man could hope to encompass. And there were so many approaches one could take. Bird flight, kites, models, full-size gliders, giant powered aircraft, wind tunnels, whirling arms, and pure theory—all had their merits and demerits: all had their secrets to unfold. Progress, painfully slow at first, was only made when individuals took it upon themselves to probe the mysteries, often at great personal risk. The greatest risks were taken by those who believed that, if man were to master the air, the time must come when he would have to meet the element on its own terms in a machine of his own creation. Those who gambled in innocence were foolhardy. Those who gambled with awareness were the true pioneers, and they should be remembered.

I am indebted to the many people who have contributed in many ways to this book. Some have provided material assistance, while others have assisted spiritually and with wise council.

John Bagley and the late Fitz Cowley were not only constant sources of help and encouragement, but also read the manuscript and offered valuable advice and suggestions. Jack Beaumont's readiness to listen and discuss problems has always been greatly appreciated.

My grateful thanks go to all of the following: Martin Andrewartha; Lord and Lady Braye; E. Grove, Jan Bird and 2d Officer S. A. Thorburn, Women's Royal Naval Service, Britannia Royal Naval College, Dartmouth; *British Aerospace News;* British Library Newspaper Library, Hendon; Bromley South Public Library; Peter Brookes, reference librarian, National Motor Museum, Beaulieu; Peter W. Brooks; Business Press International Archives; Graham Cowell; John Crerar Library, Chicago; Deutsches Museum; Sir Robin and Lady Dunn; Dick Eales; *Flight International;* the late Thora Forrester and her son, David; Harry Gadd; General Cemetery Company, London; General Register Office, London; the late Charles H. Gibbs-Smith; the late Doug Gillies, Mike Goodall; Alex Gourlay, British Broadcasting Corporation; Guildhall Library, London; Barry Gray; Norman Hall-Warren; Clive Hart; Clement Henniker Heaton; Mike Hirst; Eugene E. Husting; Institution of Mechanical Engineers; Library of Congress Manuscript Division, Washington D.C.; Alan McCandlish; Isobel McWhirter; Peter Mann; Mitchell Library, Glasgow; Frank Munger; Gill Neale, who prepared most of the diagrams; Walter Neumark; Leo Opdycke; Patent Office Library, London; Harald Penrose; Anthony Pilcher; Nancy Pilcher; Public Record Office, Kew; Registrar of Companies and Limited Partnerships; Sir George Robinson; Margaret R. Binning, Public Relations Assistant, Rolls-Royce Glasgow; Arnold Nayler and Gordon Leith, Royal Aeronautical Society Library; Royal Commonwealth Society Library; S. G. Williams, Royal Institution of Naval Architects Library; Werner Schwipps; Scottish Record Office; W. Hudson Shaw; Smithsonian Institution, Washington, D.C.; Don Storer, Royal Museum of Scotland; Science Museum Aeronautics Department, and the library; Ted Shreeve; Pat Smith, Time Publicity Service, Leicester; "Jack" Straw, Brompton Cemetery; Richard Tustian; Sue Tyler, who typed the manuscript; University of Chicago Library; University of Glasgow Library; University of London; Victoria and Albert Museum Library; A. H. Whitehouse, Divisional Administration Director and General Manager, British Aerospace Bitteswell Aerodrome, Leicestershire, and the photographic department; A. Gordon Wilson and E. Brian Wilson; J. L. Wood, Royal Museum of Scotland; Julian Wright; Sir Eric G. Yarrow.

1

To Breast the Breeze, 1867–95

Bladud, a legendary king of Britain who reigned for twenty years from 863 B.C., is reputed to have met his death in an attempt to fly from the Temple of Apollo in Trinovantum (London). He is also credited with the discovery of the healing powers of the natural hot springs at Bath, in the county of Avon, and is said to have brought that town "to perfection."[1]

Perhaps the spirit of Bladud remains in that city, for it was at 9 North Parade, Bath, that another "flying man" was born on January 16, 1867. Percy Sinclair Pilcher was the fifth and last child of Thomas Webb Pilcher, a "fundholder" (one who holds property in the public funds), and Sophia Pilcher, née Robinson. It seems that they were in lodgings at Bath, for on Percy's birth certificate his mother gave her residential address as 10 Earl's Terrace, Kensington, London.[2]

Percy's father was born in 1799 and as a comparatively young man went to Italy and settled in Rome, where he became curator of the city's British Museum, or picture gallery. An authority on Dante, he married an Italian widow, the Marquesa de San Pietri, with whom he lived until her death in 1854. They had no children.

In 1857 Thomas Webb Pilcher married the "very young and energetic" Scottish lady, Sophia Robinson. Their first child, Thomas David Pilcher, was born in Rome on July 8, 1858. A second boy, Malcolm, died as a child, and about 1860 Thomas and Sophia returned to England and settled at Harrow. Three more children followed: Violet Ada Gallier, Ella Sophia Gertrude, and, finally, Percy.[3]

On October 10, 1874, only some eight years after Percy's birth, Thomas Webb Pilcher died at Belmont, Harrow on the Hill, leaving less than £600 "all to my dear wife."[4] At this time Percy's sixteen-year-old elder brother Thomas (known as David in the family) was at Harrow school. Sophia evidently left Harrow and took the four children to Celle, near Hanover, in Germany, where she herself died in 1877. At this time Percy was ten years old. There was very little money to go around, and Thomas, as the senior member of the family at nineteen, brought his sisters and brother—all of whom now spoke German "pretty well"—back to England and put them into school. Following his "military bias," Thomas then joined the militia, entered the army, and was gazetted to the 5th (Northumberland) Fusiliers.

In 1880, when Percy was thirteen, Thomas sent him to the Admiralty to "see the Admirals," and he entered the Royal Navy as Cadet 173 on July 15. What money he and his brother could earn went toward finishing the education of Violet and Ella.[5]

Although the records dealing with Percy's childhood and education are poor, they clearly indicate that his interest in aviation had already manifested itself. His sister Ella, to whom he was very close, recalled that from his "earliest boyhood he was entirely wrapt up in the idea of flying."[6]

Percy's naval education took place on the training ship HMS *Britannia* at Dartmouth, Devon. Flying still occupied his mind, however; Ella recollected that he made "small experiments" and remembered him as a naval cadet "explaining what he believed would be the shape and working of the flying machine of the future."[7]

During his first term at the Naval College Pilcher achieved good results in his studies, placing eighth overall in his term.[8] However, once he had settled in and familiarized himself with his surroundings, his conduct fell to "fair" in the second and third terms, and an innate reaction to military discipline seems to have emerged in the guise of numerous petty misdemeanors. Percy's conduct record lists no fewer than twenty-nine "minor offences" and eleven "aggravated offences" between March 1881 and July 1882.

Despite these small blemishes on his record, Percy performed well in his studies, being well above average in his class through the four terms of training, and even restored his conduct to "good" in the fourth term. He held his eighth position in the second term and dropped to ninth in the last two terms.

HMS Britannia *at Dartmouth, Devon, in 1908. Pilcher began his naval cadet training on this vessel in July 1880. (H. F. Cowley)*

Percy's physical qualifications were considered good in the first term, and he was consistently described as "likely to be of use to the Service." At the end of his cadet training, in July 1882, Pilcher sat his final exams and was awarded a Second Class Certificate in mathematics, extra subjects, and seamanship.

From July 21 to August 18, 1882, following his final exams, Mr. Percy St. C. Pilcher, naval cadet, was "aboard" HMS *Duke of Wellington.* This was an old three-decker used as a depot ship, and seamen were held on strength while they were ashore.[9] From August 19, after being discharged from *Wellington,* Pilcher served as a cadet on HMS *Agincourt,* an iron, screw-propelled ship of 10,600 tons.[10] During this time he kept a log. After visiting Alexandria (Egypt), Malta, and Gibraltar, *Agincourt* left for Plymouth Sound on October 19, arriving on the 26th. Pilcher was discharged on November 21, and on December 9 he joined the flagship of the North American and West Indian Station, HMS *Northampton,* an armored iron frigate of 7,652 tons and 6,070 horsepower.[11]

Aboard this ship Pilcher made a long cruise in the West Indies, "from December 1882 to March 1883." The cruise took the ship down through the Leeward and Windward Islands to Port of Spain,

Trinidad, then via Grenada, Caracas, and Curaçao to Port Royal, Jamaica, which it reached on February 19. On February 24, *Northampton* sailed again, up through the Windward Passage, around the south coast of Puerto Rico, and back to Santa Cruz. The vessel reached Bermuda late in March, by which time Percy was a midshipman, having been rated as such on March 16, 1883.[12]

In late July, *Northampton* continued northward to Halifax, Nova Scotia, and during August, September, and October of 1883 it sailed on a "northern cruise" that took Percy on a round trip from Halifax to Newfoundland. From there, *Northampton* sailed across the Gulf of St. Lawrence and up the St. Lawrence River to Quebec, then back down the St. Lawrence, across the Gulf, down through the Gut of Canso between Nova Scotia and Cape Breton Island, and back to Halifax. On Wednesday, November 21, 1883, *Northampton* steamed out of Halifax Harbour bound for Bermuda, where it arrived on November 25.

During late December 1883 and early January 1884, *Northampton* sailed to St. Kitts (St. Christopher) in the Leeward Islands, where she anchored on January 8. On January 9, 1884, Percy was discharged from *Northampton* and the next day he joined HMS *Griffon,* "Borne for Instruction in Seamanship." The ship, a composite screw gun vessel of 780 tons,[13] made a cruise through the West Indies, steaming down via St. Christopher to Antigua, proceeding under sail to Montserrat, and then proceeding by "steam tactics" to Dominica, Martinique, and—partly under sail—to Barbados. On Sunday, February 10, *Griffon* was anchored in St. George's Harbour, Grenada. Pilcher was discharged from *Griffon* on March 6, 1884, and was signed back aboard HMS *Northampton* on March 7. Apart from a short spell of temporary duty on the sloop HMS *Lily,* he remained with the frigate until April 21, 1886.

Returning from leave on June 8, 1886, Pilcher joined HMS *Calypso,* a screw corvette of 2,770 tons and 3,720 horsepower serving with a training squadron at Chatham.[14] On January 1, 1887, he was discharged from *Calypso,* and on January 2 he joined HMS *Volage,* an iron screw corvette of 3,080 tons[15] "to be examined for rank of Lieutenant." He remained on *Volage* until May 12. His last discharge form is headed "Allowed to resign at own request. 18 Apl. 87." He is still listed as a midshipman.

It was customary to leave the service one rank above that attained during service, though this was not usual at the midshipman level.

A pen-and-ink sketch by Pilcher of HMS Calypso *"getting main yard fore and aft" on August 30, 1886. He served on this corvette for the second half of that year. (Author)*

However, thereafter Percy was always referred to as a "lieutenant," perhaps because he had passed his examinations just before his resignation, or because midshipman was neither a recognized commissioned rank nor a "rate."[16] The reason for his break from the navy after seven years at sea remains obscure.

It seems logical to assume that Pilcher's transatlantic travels provided him with ample opportunity to study the flight of the great seabirds. It would be obvious to him that power was not essential to enable man at least to sample the delights of flight. Likewise, his naval training in knot tying, lashing, pulley systems, and the bracing of structures was to prove invaluable in the years ahead. It was during his naval career, as well, that he met and struck up a friendship with the Honorable Adrian Verney Cave, son of the fifth Lord Braye, of whom more will be heard later.[17]

For the moment, however, Pilcher retained a link with the sea. Accompanied by Ella, he went to Glasgow, Scotland, where he apprenticed from June 1, 1887, in the engineering department of Randolph Elder & Co. (later Fairfields), a shipbuilding yard at Govan.

There he remained for two years, working his way through the engine and pattern shops and working as a draftsman until July 8, 1889.[18] During this time he became almost legendary for his ideas, and a fellow worker has described him as "a pale serious fellow, with a great bent for invention, and a brain that was razor keen."[19] Then followed five months as an apprentice moulder with Messrs. Cairns & Co. of Glasgow.[20]

Percy's next move remains something of a mystery. He has stated that he "attended classes at University College, London, in Engineering, Eng. Laboratory, etc."[21] His sister Ella has written that her brother "went to the University of London."[22] Other sources, probably taking their lead from Ella's statement, say that he "attended London University" or "studied" there.[23]

Contrary to these apparent statements of fact, the University of London informed the author: "After a search of the University records, no trace can be found of a person of this name."[24] It must therefore be assumed that Percy attended the lectures but was not officially enrolled as a student. This episode was short-lived, in any case, for about May 1890 Pilcher began working in the Engine Department Drawing Office at Southampton Naval Works Ltd., managed by John H. Biles, where he remained for eighteen months.[25] One item that survives from this sparsely recorded period is a half-size drawing—side and front elevations—for a "launch engine 5″ × 4″," inscribed "P. S. Pilcher Esq^{e}" and dated October 28, 1889.[26] There are no clues to its origin or purpose, however.

In November 1891 Percy returned with Ella to Glasgow, becoming assistant to Prof. John Biles, now newly appointed as part-time Elder professor of naval architecture and marine engineering at Glasgow University.[27] In 1935 Ella wrote: "He had been working for Sir John Biles at Woolston [Southampton], & went up to help him. They made a number of tests of the resistance offered by water to differently shaped bows of ships—with model yachts & of these Percy was at first in charge."[28] An 1895 reference describes Pilcher as "Assistant Lecturer to the Naval Architecture and Marine Engineering Class at the Glasgow University, and Draftsman in the shipbuilding firm of Messrs. J. & G. Thomson, Clydebank,"[29] so he was obviously putting his time to good use.

The Pilchers were "bright, clever and attractive and made many friends."[30] Ella is remembered in the family as being "extremely energetic and restless,''[31] and was ''an accomplished songstress.''[32] Percy was enterprising, energetic, and a bit of a dreamer, according to family recollections. Sam Mavor, of the Glasgow engineering firm Mavor & Coulson Ltd., wrote that Percy ''was equipped with ingenuity and resource, technical ability and knowledge of scientific principles,'' and displayed ''vision, courage, tenacity . . . physical fitness . . . exceptional mental and nervous alertness.''[33]

It was during Pilcher's time at the university that his interest in flying began to grow. As the classes met only in the winter months, Percy had the long summer holidays available for his own interests.[34]

On November 2, 1893, he was granted his first two British patents, numbers 20,767 and 20,768. His address was given as 95 Philbeck Gardens, South Kensington, London SW—a family address. Patent 20,767 was for a simple case made from tinplate ''or other suitable material,'' designed to be hung upon a ''gas bracket, nail, or other convenient projection'' to hold a matchbox. Slots in the bottom and sides of the case allowed the matchbox to be pushed out. Patent 20,768 was equally simple—it was for circular covers for glasses and cups to keep their contents ''warm and free from dust.''[35]

The following year, 1894, Pilcher was granted Provisional Specification No. 15614 of August 17 for ''Improvements in Signalling Apparatus.'' This related to signaling devices attached to the anchor line of a captive balloon, but it was subsequently abandoned.[36] On November 2, 1894, he applied for Patent 21,024, concerning ''captive balloons, kites, etc.,'' but the precise nature of the patent is unknown, for it was again abandoned.[37]

Pilcher read ''extensively,''[38] and we can be certain that his attention was drawn to aeronautical items in the popular press during the 1890s, especially those concerning the work of two prominent aviation pioneers, Hiram Stevens Maxim in England and Otto Lilienthal in Germany. Both men had built and tested full-size aircraft, but their respective approaches to the problem of heavier-than-air flight differed greatly.

Whereas Maxim had elected to build a massive 104-foot span biplane-multiplane powered by a pair of 180-horsepower steam engines, Lilienthal, after years of studying bird flight with his brother Gustav, had decided to work at the opposite end of the scale, flying simply built unpowered hang gliders in an attempt to evolve a controllable device before adding a prime mover.

Hiram Maxim's airplane test rig on its track at Baldwyns Park, Kent, in 1894. (H. F. Cowley)

Years of trial and error brought their reward, and in 1891 Otto made his first successful gliding flight, in his No. 3 glider. Various designs followed, all light structures of willow and fabric, culminating in the No. 11 "Normal-Segelapparat" or "standard" monoplane glider of 1894. This became the first heavier-than-air aircraft to be produced in quantity, Lilienthal supplying them to other experimenters at a cost of £25 each—equivalent to more than £500 ($745) today.[39]

Accounts of Lilienthal's flying experiments illustrated by photographs of the German pioneer sailing through the air were widely published, and Percy Pilcher decided that it would be "most interesting to try and copy, and to try and proceed further with what he had done."[40]

He began by building and testing model gliders in the lodgings that he shared with his sister Ella in Byres Road, but objections from his landlady forced him to seek alternative accommodation. The new lodgings were in Kersland Street.[41] Percy was fortunate to be granted the loan of a large room under the roof of the university—reportedly one of the natural philosophy rooms—for use as a workshop when the university was closed.[42]

Although none of the correspondence between Pilcher and Lilienthal is known to survive, Percy must have been in touch with the

Otto Lilienthal (1848–96), the great German pioneer whose experiments with hang gliders inspired Pilcher. This portrait was taken in 1895, the year that Pilcher built his first machine. (Smithsonian Institution)

Lilienthal flying his No. 6 glider at Rhinow in 1893. (Werner Schwipps)

German pioneer early in 1895, because he made plans to visit him in Berlin in the spring. However, he began work on his first full-size man-carrying glider early in the year. His purpose in beginning its construction before seeing the Lilienthal machines firsthand was "to get the greatest advantage from any original ideas I might have."[43]

This glider became known as the "Bat"—possibly because it looked, as the *Glasgow Evening Citizen* noted, "like a huge bat with outstretched wings."[44] Designed to be easily transportable when broken down, it comprised five basic components—a body piece, a "triangle," two wings, and the fin. The central component was the body piece (11 feet 8 inches long and 2 feet 4 inches wide),[45] in which stood the pilot, whose forearms were slipped through leather sleeves on the longitudinal members, each hand grasping a rigid handle. The legs of the triangle passed through "quadrant-shaped" steel plates screwed to the body piece and to the front spar of each wing. The apex and lower corners of the triangle formed attachment points for the upper and lower wing-bracing wires. Nainsook, used for light racing sails and "generally manufactured in India,"[46] covered the wings and fin and was deemed to be "the most suitable material to be had at a modest price."[47] Ella's skills at the sewing machine came to the fore in the shaping of these surfaces.[48]

Behind the main spar and radiating rearwards from the innermost front corner of each wing were four light ribs, each of which was braced with piano wire at three points above and below to the aforementioned triangle. The front spars crossed one another in front of the triangle, their extremities being lashed to the opposite sides. The roots of each of the eight ribs were finished with two small steel plates, through which passed a bolt securing them to the steel quadrant on the triangle. Simply by undoing the lacing that held the fabric to the body piece, one could fold the whole wing surface forward "like a fan"[49] and wrap it around each main spar like a furled sail. A long bamboo rod with the end bent around and covered with fabric formed the fin and completed the structure. There was no tailplane.

Built principally of Riga pine, the finished Bat weighed 44 pounds empty and was designed to bear from 180 to 200 pounds in flight.[50] A notable feature of the assembled glider was the acute dihedral angle of the wings, the tips being some 4 feet above the roots. Pilcher incorporated this angle because he "believed that it would facilitate transverse balance,"[51] "just as a kite is stable sideways when it is of this shape, or as a piece of paper folded to a V-shape will always

The acute dihedral of the Bat's wings is apparent in this front view, with Pilcher, wearing his polo belt, demonstrating the pilot's position. (Author)

A three-quarter rear view of the Bat in its first form. The lack of a tailplane is conspicuous. The two men are unidentified. (Author)

fall on the folded edge."[52] It is uncertain whether he proofed the fabric of this first machine to render it waterproof (and airtight), but by the end of the year he was certainly doing so. After the "sails" were completed, they were dipped first in a saturated solution of sugar of lead (lead acetate, which was used as a mordant in the dyeing and printing of textiles), and then straight into a saturated solution of alum (a double sulphate of aluminum and potassium, also used as a mordant in dyeing as well as in sizing paper and fireproofing). When the wings were dry, Pilcher stated, "Water if poured on to them will run off as if they had been oiled." The only side effect was very slight shrinkage; there was no perceptible increase in weight.[53]

Testing of the Bat was delayed by Pilcher's first visit to Germany, in April, to meet Lilienthal and to see him fly. By this time the German engineer was gliding from a 50-foot conical artificial hill (the "Fliegeberg"), which he had had thrown up at Lichterfelde in 1894, using earth from canal excavations close to his home. He had incorporated a "cave" in its peak in which to house his machines.[54] Pilcher found that "the country round is as flat as the sea, and there is not a house or tree near it [the hill] to make the wind unsteady, so that this was an ideal practising ground."[55]

Helped by his knowledge of the language, the disciple learned a great deal from his master. Lilienthal had made an unprecedented study of bird flight over some twenty-five years and had published his now-classic book, *Der Vogelflug als Grundlage der Fliegekunst (Bird Flight as the Basis of the Flying Art).*[56] Octave Chanute, in his great and still unsurpassed chronicle of aviation's early development, *Progress in Flying Machines,* acknowledged Lilienthal's work as being "among the most systematic and carefully conducted series of experiments that have ever been made in the direction of artificial flight."[57] "Dexterity alone," Otto wrote, "invests the native inhabitants of the air with superiority over man in that element,"[58] and he then set about attaining that dexterity by careful and progressively longer flights. The cambered wings of his hang gliders, based on those of birds, enabled him to make repeated flights with a descent angle of 1 in 6, and sometimes as low as 1 in 10, when some 300 feet was covered from takeoff to touchdown.[59]

Lilienthal believed that he and his brother had discovered the "real secret of flying" in the "slight curvature of the wing," "as a logical deduction from the flight of birds."[60] Unbeknownst to him, however, Sir George Cayley had speculated on the superiority of cambered surfaces in the 1800s, and at least two others had made the same discovery at about the same time as he had, each of them unaware that others were treading the same path.

In 1884 an Englishman, Horatio Frederick Phillips, had patented the "dipping" edge, the diagrams in the patent depicting several forms of arched wing section.[61] Although Phillips's theory was inadequate, he is given credit for being the first to establish the form of the airfoil. From Lilienthal's writings, it appears that he was unaware of Phillips's work and had discovered the advantages of the "curved wing" quite independently during 1890–94. However, as that great pioneer of aerodynamics F. W. Lanchester has pointed out, "There is no evidence to show that Lilienthal possessed more than a practical acquaintance with the arched form."[62] Lanchester continues: "About the same time as Lilienthal was at work [I] succeeded in evolving the arched form, or dipping front edge, purely from theoretical considerations, at the time having no knowledge of the previous work of Phillips or the experiments then being conducted by Lilienthal. [I] first formulated [this] theory in 1892."[63]

While Lanchester remained earthbound and progressed by theory, Lilienthal believed that progress should be made in practice, carefully and by stages, beginning with small unpowered machines carrying one man. Some of his reasoning went as follows: "The increasing size of the apparatus makes the construction more difficult in securing lightness in the machine; therefore the building of small apparatuses is to be recommended. . . . experiments in actual flight will only be instructive when a man participates in the flight, and maintains stable equilibrium at will. . . . Gradual development of flight should begin with the simplest apparatus and movements, and without the complication of dynamic means."[64] The German's greatest error lay in his conviction that, when power came to be applied to propel the machine, it would be used to flap the wings or "portions" of them. He seems not to have considered the airscrew.

When Pilcher went to Lichterfelde in April 1895, Lilienthal was flying his No. 11 monoplane, which weighed 56 pounds and had a wing area of 105 square feet. Percy described the glider as being "roughly made, almost entirely of peeled willow sticks, covered with cotton shirting."[65] Crude though these structures may have been, they worked, and Percy was able to obtain firsthand advice on their management. By shifting his body fore and aft, and thereby adjusting the machine's center of gravity, Lilienthal could make his glider accelerate or slow down. A degree of longitudinal stability was provided by the tailplane, which was set at a marked negative angle to the wings and therefore had a constant download imposed upon it. The dihedral angle of the wings was far less than in the Bat, and by swinging his torso and legs to the left or right Lilienthal could bring down a raised wing or even accomplish tentative turns. This was not an instinctive action, for it was the pilot's natural tendency to extend his legs toward the low wing, especially when near the ground. However, this would only exacerbate the situation, and the pilot had to train himself to react by swinging his legs *away* from the low wing, thereby lowering the high wing and regaining level flight.

Landing, too, demanded a novel technique. If a landing was made at flying speed (about 25 miles per hour), it was impossible for the pilot to avoid being dragged helplessly along or even being bowled over in his machine. The birds supplied the answer, still in use with modern hang gliders. A few feet above the ground before touchdown, the pilot shifts his weight backward. This effectively stalls the machine in the air, allowing it to drop to the ground with virtually no forward motion at all.

Other perils were waiting aloft—lose forward speed and the glider could slip backward or stall and plummet out of control; lower the wings too much in front in an attempt to regain speed, and an irrecoverable nosedive could result.

When Pilcher described his own glider to Lilienthal, the German was dismayed to learn that his disciple had omitted to fit a tailplane. He urged the young Englishman to do so, as it was "absolutely necessary," but Pilcher firmly refused to believe that it was.[66] The reasoning is obscure. Pilcher's own observation of birds would have shown him that they invariably have a horizontal tail surface but no fin. Why he elected to adopt the opposite arrangement remains a mystery.

Upon his return to Glasgow, Pilcher prepared to test the Bat, which was probably ready by the end of May. Lacking a man-made purpose-built hill like Lilienthal's, he had to settle for the best natural slopes that he could find, and the chosen site was at Wallacetown Farm, just inland and east from Cardross, Dumbartonshire, on the north bank of the Clyde.[67] The hills in the area were not exceptionally steep (the ground was 250–400 feet above sea level) and faced in any wind direction from south to west. Moreover, the slopes faced the Firth of Clyde, and the prevailing wind, coming across that expanse of water, was as free from turbulence as could be hoped, although the area was squally. The site was sufficiently remote to allow escape from spectators, but it was reasonably accessible by railway or cart. Nonetheless, it must have been no easy journey for someone laden down with glider components.

On a calm day in June a hill was selected sloping toward the prevailing wind, and Pilcher stepped into the Bat and ran down the hill. The glider "took its own entire weight, but little more," and when the foot of the slope was reached it "invariably pitched forwards, bringing the experimenter to his knees with considerable force, and often running the bowsprits deep into the ground." In an effort to correct this problem, Pilcher moved the handgrips back in the body piece in an attempt to adjust the center of gravity. However, on the second day of tests this adjustment only helped a little, and the inventor was forced to accept that Lilienthal was right.[68] "Without the horizontal rudder," he said later, "I was able to do nothing—it was not until I had put on the horizontal rudder that I was able to leave the ground at all."[69]

A completely new tail, comprising a circular tailplane bisected by a circular fin and attached to the body piece by a curved bamboo boom, was next fitted.

"At the next trial," reported the *Practical Engineer* in its December 6, 1895, issue, "there was a nice wind blowing up the hill, and Mr. Pilcher having rigged at the foot of the hill, in the shelter, backed up to the summit, keeping the front edge of the wings down, that the machine might not lift. Having reached the top, he held the wings up a little in front, and was immediately taken up 4 ft. into the air, remained poised for a few seconds, and then, throwing his weight forward, came down on exactly the same spot as he had been taken up from; but on landing the machine was caught by a side puff, and was blown over, breaking the front spar in the starboard wing."[70]

Thus, for one brief, exhilarating moment, Pilcher experienced his first tentative flight in a glider of his own design and construction—and also his first crash, albeit a minor one from which he emerged unscathed. He was undeterred, and probably elated. The report continues: "This mishap was quickly sufficiently repaired for him to make some more trials. He ran down the hill several times, taking leaps of up to 50 ft. in length, and in height about 2 ft. or 3 ft. from the ground; but it being turned over again, the machine was too much injured to be mended on the field. The increased success was evidently due to the new rudder."[71]

A report in the *American Engineer and Railroad Journal* for August 1895 stated that the wind was blowing at 15 miles per hour and was "unfortunately rather puffy," and that the first "flight" had lasted some ten seconds.

Sadly, the date of this significant event in British aviation has passed unrecorded, but it most probably occurred between late June and mid-July. Pilcher repeated these experiments the following week "with much the same success, but again broke one of the spars. He

Another angle on the Bat. Note that the fabric is beneath the ribs, a system that was reversed on the Gull. Ella is in the center of the group, Percy on the right. (Author)

Percy and Ella Pilcher demonstrate the Bat's portability at Cardross in 1895. Percy carries the furled wings and the bracing triangle, while Ella totes the tailboom and fin and the body piece. (Author)

A good headwind could be exploited to do the work of carrying the modified Bat, with its bisecting circular fin and tailplane, back uphill after a glide. Percy demonstrates the technique in this 1895 photograph, taken near Auchensail. (Author)

Pilcher prepares to fly the interim Bat, 1895. (Author)

attributes these accidents," continues the American report, "to the fact of his wings being so much elevated at the points that a puff of wind from the side can get under one wing and raise it while the other is sheltered. Therefore, before mending the machine described above, he has determined to build another on the same principles, but of entirely different structure, and with the wings very much less elevated."[72]

Pilcher was certainly not at all happy with the excessive dihedral angle of the Bat's wings. "The upturned wings were all very well if there was no wind, or if the wind was steady," he stated, "but if the wind shifted slightly sideways, and came on to one side of the machine, it would tend to raise the windward wing and depress the lee one, and capsize me sideways, which nearly always meant a breakage in the machine."[73] This problem was particularly noticeable on the ground. "If one were far in the air," he later wrote, "one would have time to recover, but when standing on the ground a machine which is stiff sideways will always get capsized by a change in the direction of the wind."[74]

In an attempt to resolve this difficulty, Percy set aside the Bat and designed a second glider. The restrictions imposed on the design by the need to make it transportable were avoided by renting "a farmhouse with a very large, empty barn at Cardross" (actually it was located at Auchensail, now Low Auchensail, to the north of Cardross).[75] This meant that component parts could be built in Glasgow and taken to the barn for final assembly. The completed glider could then be "hangared" permanently in the barn at Auchensail.

Percy planned to install an engine in this machine after the initial gliding trials, and to this end it was made much stronger and was consequently heavier when completed (weighing some 80 pounds empty) and had a greater wing area (170 square feet).[76] Structurally, too, it was very different from the Bat. The body comprised two side frames employing Warren girder-type construction—almost certainly the first application of such construction in an aircraft—with spacers between them allowing enough width for Percy's shoulders. It was built entirely of white pine.[77] The square-cut wing was based upon five transverse spars, or ribs, of bamboo—a notable departure from the Bat's radial ribs—and the wing curvature was formed by the curve of the top longerons of the fuselage, across which the spars were laid. A pair of chordwise ribs were also provided on each side. Two kingposts were attached to the body at about one-third chord and protruded

Ella Pilcher, who helped to sew the wings for her brother's gliders and was a staunch supporter in his experiments. (Author)

some 3 feet above the wings. From these, bracing wires were attached to two points on each spar to support the wing at rest, and several "lift" wires ran from the lower longerons out to the wings. A bamboo-framed tail similar to that of the Bat, comprising two discs crossing at their centers, was wire-braced to the rear end of the innermost chordwise rib and to the body.

The wings were completely flat transversely and, in an attempt to compensate for the lack of inherent stability, Pilcher positioned himself much lower in the frame, his forearms passing through sleeves on the lower longerons. Thus the wings were at eye level, and all of the pilot's weight was below the wings. This position provided a great deal of pendulum stability.

When one sees this machine from the rear, with its stiff, carapace-like wing, it is easy to understand why Pilcher dubbed it the Beetle.

Unfortunately, the Beetle proved every bit as ungainly as it looked, despite its improved method of construction. First of all, its excessive weight made it tiring to handle. Second, Pilcher very quickly discovered that the low center of gravity resulting from the high wing allowed him "very little control" over the machine. "A sudden puff

The lack of dihedral and the pilot's low position are evident in this study of Pilcher in the Beetle in front of the Auchensail farmhouse about June or July 1895. (Author)

A three-quarter rear view of the Beetle reveals its five spanwise "ribs," or spars, and the great wing area—170 square feet. The fabric is again beneath the ribs. (Author)

The Bat "Mark 3," with its deeply arched wings, rides the breeze while Percy holds the forward extensions of the body piece. The ribs are still in sleeves above the fabric. (Author)

In this front view, with Pilcher on the right, the string tensioners are visible where the bracing wires meet their wing attachment points. (Author)

of wind," he wrote, "would carry the machine backwards, leaving me, because of my weight, as it were, behind, and it is only by slipping out of the machine when it was above my head that I several times avoided going head over heels backwards with it."[78]

Disenchanted by this experience, Percy returned to the Bat. During the first trials he had broken so many front spars that he decided to replace the inflexible pine by a more supple wood.[79] He also arched the spars downward transversely to reduce the dihedral considerably, the tips being only some 6 inches above the roots.[80] In this form the Bat also seems to have been fitted with a refinement to the bracing that later became standard practice. Instead of attaching the wires directly to the ribs, Pilcher made them short and linked the wire loop in the end of the bracing wire and the anchoring loop on the rib by string or twine. Like the turnbuckle of much later bracing systems, this arrangement allowed the wire tension to be easily adjusted by tightening the string link; thus the wire itself did not have to be untwisted and rewound.

"With the wings turned down," reported the *Practical Engineer,* "the machine has no real stability of its own—that is, it has practically no tendency to right itself if inclined to one side when head to wind in a breeze; but at the same time, if placed not exactly into wind, it has very little tendency to capsize. Both transverse and longitudinal balance have then, with the turned down wings, to be maintained by the operator moving his weight about in the machine."[81]

Once again theory was put into practice on the gentle slopes at Cardross. By staying at the Auchensail farmhouse during the summer vacation, Percy was able to practice "almost daily,"[82] although the winds were usually squally. Needless to say, he envied Lilienthal his prime testing hill with its steady winds. In late August and early September the testing of the modified Bat began. Pilcher stated that, with the lowered wing tips, "I obtained by far my best results."[83] The modification allowed him to make trials in stronger winds than before, and on September 12 he was "picked up from the ground, taken up 12 ft., and landed after spending nearly half a minute in the air; and later on the same day—after the wind had gone down a little—a line was tied on to the front of the machine, and a man ran with this; the result was that the machine, with Mr. Pilcher in it, went 20 ft. into the air, and was away from the ground nearly a minute."[84]

Pilcher reported in *Nature* magazine,

> With this original apparatus [I] have been picked up by a puff of wind over and again, sometimes as much as 12 ft. above the spot I was lifted from, and put down again on exactly the same place. At other times, when there has not been so much wind, I ran to meet the wind with the front of the wings depressed somewhat, so that my weight is only partially taken by the wings, and in this way I am . . . able to run very much faster than without the wings; then raising the front edge a little,

Pilcher makes a towed flight in the Bat "Mark 3" in 1895, one of the earliest photographs depicting a manned heavier-than-air aircraft in flight in the British Isles. The boy with the tow line is on the left and Ella is on the right. (Author)

> I am able to take a longer soar down a slight incline. The only slopes on which I was able to practise, were not steep enough to make it possible for me to soar for any great distance; and therefore I have at times, on days when the wind was fairly steady, attached a string to the front of the machine, with which a boy has run and kept me in the air for about half a minute. I never used a line when there was enough wind to pick me up without forward movement, on account of the strong winds at Cardross being so very squally."[85]

These early towed glider flights were the distant forerunners of the modern winch tow, and Pilcher was to make increasing use of the technique. Two photographs taken during these tests are the earliest pictures of a heavier-than-air aircraft airborne in the British Isles.

The *Practical Engineer* reported that the experiments became

> much more certain as the experimenter gained experience—*i.e.* when he had gained sufficient quickness and experience to be ready in any crisis instinctively to bring the whole or part of his weight, as the case might require, to bear on the side of the machine that was caught by the wind, or, of course, fore or aft, if need be.

> The chief difficulties of balance are met with on attempting to land after a flight. When there is a good deal of wind, and the machine has been lifted up and set down again on the same spot, landing is comparatively easy. With a little practice the transverse balance can be maintained, and the longitudinal balance is easy; but after a flight against a very slight wind, or in almost calm weather—*i.e.* when the speed over the ground has been great—the landing presents great difficulties. The wings must be raised in front to stop the forward motion and prevent tipping over forwards. . . . Mr. Pilcher's best results have always been made with a wind of about 18 to 23 miles [per hour], blowing straight up the hill. . . . He finds it best, if possible, to get a breeze straight off the sea, for any building or wooded land to windward is apt to make the wind unreliable.
>
> From these results Mr. Pilcher has learnt that with a total weight of 200 lb. and a sail area of 150 square feet, in order to lift, the machine must go through the air at a speed of rather more than 20 miles an hour. If the wind has this speed, the experimenter can stand still, and, lifting his wings, will be picked up off the ground; if, however, the breeze is less, it must be made up for by running hard down the hill, the wings being feathered, when they offer scarcely any resistance to the wind, until the necessary speed has been reached; then, lifting them in front, the machine rises into the air. Sometimes a small line has been tied to the machine, with which a man has run. . . . On some occasions Mr. Pilcher has been lifted 20 ft., and taken over a surface of 200 or more feet, before touching the ground again.[86]

The need to "rear up" and stall the machine when landing in low winds had led Lilienthal to fit a tailplane that was hinged at its leading edge, allowing the trailing edge to rise freely, though wires prevented it from falling below the desired negative angle. This meant that when the pilot tipped back the glider, the tail simply "gave" and offered no resistance, thereby making the action more rapid. By restraining it from traveling downward, the wires avoided a nose-over. Pilcher had adopted a similar system on his bisected circular tailplanes.[87]

The major task of learning to fly was hampered by relatively small but frustrating problems: "the difficulty of finding hills which face the wind on different days, and moving the machine from one field to the other, over hedges, ditches, gates, &c., often after it is rigged, and the great objection horses and all cattle have to the machine."[88]

Percy had to stop experimenting at the end of September "on account of the unsettled winds and short days"[89] (and probably because of the beginning of the university's winter term). However, he thought that "so far as I have gone, my work has been rewarded with as much success as could possibly have been hoped for."[90] Landing had been learned painfully: "Sometimes it is very difficult to tilt the machine up suddenly—I have landed at full length on my stomach trying to get my weight far enough back & yet landed so fast that the machine has slid some yards on the ground before stopping."[91] The lowered wing tips were also more prone to damage, and breakages were not uncommon.

To support his back while controlling the gliders and bringing them in to land, Percy had from the outset worn a wide polo player's belt. Some 5 inches deep and with three front-fastening leather straps, it was buckled tightly round his waist before flying. He also tucked his trousers into long, thick woollen socks.

In a report of Pilcher's experiments entitled "Aerial Navigation," published in its issue for October 19, 1895, the *Glasgow Evening Citizen* revealed some of the pioneer's plans for the winter and the following year.

> It is Mr. Pilcher's intention . . . to still further extend the area of the wings on his next machine to 300 square feet—exactly double the dimension of his first.
>
> In the coming winter he intends to construct a small engine which will develop two horse power, and will be worked by means of carbonic acid gas carried compressed in a liquid form. This will enable him to work the engine for about a minute. Mr. Pilcher, therefore, hopes by next year to be able to fly, at all events, some hundred yards.
>
> The engine, which will run at a given number of revolutions, will be placed in the centre of the machine, and will be so connected as to drive a screw propeller of about 3 ft. diameter placed under each wing.
>
> These should give a thrust of about 20 lbs. [*sic*]—that is about one-tenth of the total weight of the machine which will weigh altogether about 70 lbs. This, it is expected, should float the machine at a speed of 25 or 30 miles an hour.

A sheet of sketches and calculations now in the library of the Royal Aeronautical Society depicts the preliminary outline of this machine, which Pilcher was to dub the "Gull." In addition to tentative front and side elevations, the sheet contains rough sketches for the tiny carbonic acid gas engine. Accompanying calculations allow for 1-inch diameter cylinders, 2-inch stroke, and two cylinders producing 1 horsepower at 1,000 revolutions per minute; 1¼-inch diameter, 2½-inch stroke producing 1½ horsepower at 1,000 revolutions; and also for a unit of unspecified dimensions producing 2 horsepower with a gas flow of 600 cubic feet per minute.[92]

The idea of the 2-horsepower carbonic acid gas motor was not original. Otto Lilienthal had built just such a unit to power the ornithoptering wing tip "driving feathers" of his No. 16 monoplane, built in 1893 and tested in 1894.[93] Percy had obviously learned of this during his visit to Germany, for he described its working in a lecture in December 1895: "When ever he [Lilienthal] touches a valve with his thumb a single acting cylinder gives a stroke—this makes the drivers flap down by means of the bell-crank levers . . . elastic connections at the top bring the drivers up again—this apparatus was tried last year and unfortunately broke owing to technical defects—before any good results were obtained."[94] It is unlikely that "good results" would ever have been forthcoming, for 2 horsepower would have been totally inadequate, even driving Percy's screw propellers, let alone Lilienthal's crude flapping feathers.

Pilcher must have set to work very quickly on the Gull, with its 300 square feet of wing area. Light winds in the summer of 1895 had precluded the possibility of gliding on some occasions, and the new machine was specifically designed with calm days in mind.[95]

Once again, several refinements and "new" constructional ideas were incorporated. Although the glider employed the now-familiar bisecting-disc tail surfaces, its body piece was a simple wire-braced box girder of longerons and stringers, tapered fore and aft. Attached to this, and extending out to each side below the wing surface, was a "subframe" consisting of short upper and lower spars. At the tips of these spars were two tall vertical bamboo kingposts that extended up through the wing on each side, about one-third of the chord back from the leading edge, and were linked at the top by a bracing wire. Radial ribs were again used, but these now pivoted on the kingposts above the top spars. Only "landing wires" were fitted, three to each rib, and these were anchored to the tops of the kingposts. The tail was also braced. Like the Bat, the Gull, which reportedly weighed 55 pounds and had a loading of only 0.7 pound per square foot with pilot,[96] could be broken down for transport. The body piece and tail were detached, and the wings were folded back around the posts.

By now, however, it was too late in the year to test such a lightly loaded machine, and in his lecture to Glasgow University's Students Engineering Society on December 12 (to be covered in greater detail shortly), Pilcher stated that the Gull had "not yet been really tried—will wait for very calm settled weather."[97]

The word "really" in the above quotation suggests that a tentative trial had been made. This idea is supported by two photographs of the Gull with its starboard wing damaged in an original album of Pilcher photographs in the author's possession. The fact that the wing covering looks clean and new and that Percy is wearing a pullover indicates that the pictures were taken late in the year. Of additional interest is a poem stuck to the facing page and dated October 11, 1895:

Elegy

Oh! I would I were a seagull
Or bird of any kind,
(For whether owl or other fowl
I would not greatly mind);
I would quit this world plebeian,
I would scale the empyrean,
And the moon and sun I would soon outrun
And leave them far behind.

If I had but sturdy plumage
I'd flee this slavish crowd;
With tit and wren, with hawk and hen
I'd course amid the cloud.
But it still, alas! doth fail me,
For the sour fates hot assail me,
And with jealous eye they observe, and try
To slay my project proud.

"In wreck their beauty lies." Pilcher stands beside the damaged Gull, ca. October 1895. The absence of a crossbar between the kingposts suggests that this picture depicts the Gull in its earliest form. (Author)

For I built me stately pinions
Like snowy canopies,
To breast the breeze and top the trees
And wheel about the skies.
I spread each spotless feather,
—Ah me, the traitor weather!—
For there came one puff; it was quite enough:
In wreck their beauty lies.

So with purple oaths assist me
My fury to assuage,
For I cannot hope my tongue will cope
With the measure of my rage.
Since up here I must *seem proper;*
(If my sister swears, I stop her)
Yet my studied smile cloaks a depth of guile
That no Devil's plumb could gauge.

Although this delightful—if somewhat amateurish—verse on the frustrations of flying is written in the first person, the original is not in Percy's handwriting, and it may well have been written down by Ella. However, whether she or Percy was the author remains a mystery. The most appealing possibility is that Ella composed it to "assuage" her brother's fury after crashing his newly built Gull. The reference to Percy having to "seem proper" in the eyes of their companions is a wonderful insight into his reluctance to conform to a stereotyped university image.

Prof. John Biles recalled an approach for assistance that Pilcher made to Lord Kelvin, the university's professor of natural philosophy:

> He [Pilcher] was one of the few men I have met who had no sense of fear. . . . I was deterred from helping him as much as I ought to have done by a fear of the risks that he ran. He at one time talked to Lord Kelvin about helping him: Lord Kelvin spoke to me about it, and said that on no account would he help him, nor should I, as he would certainly break his neck.[98]

Pilcher's sister Ella wrote that "Lord Kelvin used to send chaffing messages to Percy about flying, but he also gave us the use of a very large room at the top of the University to work in when the University was closed."[99] Unfortunately, Kelvin was not the best person to approach on such a matter. The following year, when invited by Maj. B. F. S. Baden-Powell to join the Aeronautical Society of Great Britain, Kelvin replied on December 8 that "I have not the smallest molecule of faith in aerial navigation other than ballooning or of expectation of good results from any of the trials we hear of. So you will understand that I would not care to be a member of the Aeronautical Society."[100]

By late October 1895 Pilcher had moved to lodgings at 12 Wilson Street, in Glasgow's Hillhead district, a little further from the university than either of his previous addresses in the city. From here he wrote to London on October 23. The addressee was possibly Maj. B. F. S. Baden-Powell, brother of the Chief Scout and member of the council of the struggling Aeronautical Society of Great Britain (ASGB). Baden-Powell was an enthusiastic kite flyer and a prolific writer on aeronautics.

Pilcher wrote that he was "very pleased with the success I have had—My new machine with 300 sq. ft. area [the Gull] is quite another shape . . . and as far as I can judge is an improvement." He enclosed two photographs, commenting, "you will see one of the wings is broken in the photo with the sails [wings] set," and adding, "I think you will find one of these machines very much easier to handle than kites in the ordinary sense of the word. If you think of experimenting with a machine of this kind," Percy concluded, "I will get one made for you if you would like me to do so. Workmanship is a good deal cheaper up here than close to London."[101]

In its issue of December 6, the *Practical Engineer* reported that Pilcher was working on yet another glider of similar construction to that of the Gull, but with only 170 square feet of "sail"—the same as in the Beetle. "Both [the Gull and the new machine]," the magazine stated, "are designed so that it would be possible to add a small engine in front of the experimenter, to work a screw propeller placed under each wing." This machine was to have an undercarriage. A specification and drawings survive in the Royal Aeronautical Society for two wheels 9 inches in diameter "for P. S. Pilcher, 12, Wilson St., Hillhead." They were to have brass bushes and solid rubber tires ½-inch thick and ¾-inch across. The wood was to be "very dry plane tree."[102]

Pilcher hoped to display his new glider at his lecture to the Glasgow University Students Engineering Society on December 12, but it was not ready in time.[103] The lecture went ahead nonetheless. It was Pilcher's first, and the first by any Englishman who had made repeated flights as the pilot of a heavier-than-air aircraft. One can't help but wonder whether the students had their tongues in their cheeks when they asked this lecturer, with his eccentric pastime, to speak before them. However, if they had expected to be amused they would have been disappointed, for the talk, although entertaining, was thoroughly practical.

After opening his address with the announcement that "the history of experiments with flying machines is more or less a history of disasters," Percy added, "contrary to the ordinary state of things the aeronautical monomaniac frequently overlooks the fall in the joy that he was a sufficient height off the ground to get one—He comforts himself for bumps and buffets by saying, as would-be riders say, that falls are the first steps to success."[104]

He then went on to mention two early predecessors, Roger Bacon and the "tower-jumping" Jean Baptiste Dante of Perugia. Next he covered the experiments of the French sailor Jean-Marie Le

Bris, who, in 1854, had made trials with an "artificial albatross" of 50-foot span and was said to have reached 300 feet and covered 600 feet—with a carter suspended underneath by the release rope! After referring to later trials by Le Bris in 1867, Pilcher leapfrogged succeeding experimenters to concentrate on the work of his mentor, Otto Lilienthal. He showed illustrations of a No. 11 glider supplied to "Mr. Bennett of Oxford" for £25 (this machine will reappear later in this story) and slides of Lilienthal in various flying attitudes. Pilcher described the control: "Slide 5 shows the machine in a critical position—He has got the machine too much up in front—it has lost its forward motion—and consequently his legs are thrown very far forward to get the CG forward so as to incline the machine down again—as one of the great dangers with a soaring machine is losing forward speed & slipping backwards."

Percy had received letters, papers, and press clippings from Otto in the preceding months[105] and was able to provide informed comment on the German's progress. Reference was made to a successful 90-degree turn accomplished in May and to the aforementioned powered glider, which had a sufficient store of compressed gas for "nearly half a minute" of horizontal flight.

Turning his attention to the scientific side of the subject, Pilcher described the forces acting on flat and curved surfaces—lift and "drift"—or drag, as it is now known. He emphasized Lilienthal's important "discovery" that "a slightly curved surface is very much better for wings than a flat surface." Lilienthal's tests had not been of sufficient accuracy to determine the optimum curvature for best performance. In fact, Pilcher stated,

> the effect of curvature is much the same whether the curve is a circular arc—or whether it has more curvature in front or behind—or whether the curvature is prac[tically] circular underneath & thickened at the top more at the front edge as a bird's wing . . . The exact effect of differential curvatures is . . . not known at all clearly.

It is obvious that many of the criteria were established more by in-flight observation than by scientific experiment. For instance, he stated that he believed the center of lift of a surface with a maximum depth of curvature equal to one-twelfth or one-fifteenth of its chord would be about one-twelfth of the chord in front of the center point: "I gather this from the position of my weight in soaring machines when they have been balanced—& from the position of Herr Lilienthal in his machine."

To reduce the fore and aft travel of the center of lift, Pilcher suggested that the wing could be split into "several short ones." We have no drawing of his proposal, but it seems to refer to a staggered tandem multiplane, for he states: "In order that the lift of the after surfaces shall remain practically uninjured by the surfaces in front—the spaces between the surfaces must be at least as great as the length [chord] of each. So to obtain the same area the total length [overall chord] will be practically doubled." "When a surface is split up into small parts—it is better to drop the after ones a little . . . this gives them more solid air to work in."

The alternative was, of course, "superposed" surfaces, as in a biplane. Pilcher alluded to the tests of models by Prof. Samuel Pierpont Langley of the Smithsonian Institution in Washington, D.C., which had proved the practicability of the idea, but warned that "the great objection to this system is that if forward speed be lost there will be practically no parachute action—to check a fall—and regaining forward speed would be a much more difficult matter."

Next, Percy spoke about the materials of which wings could be made, referring to experiments made by Hiram Maxim to determine the lift and drag of a steel frame covered with different materials. This led to a discussion on the best means of tensioning and waterproofing "sails" (Pilcher's formula for the latter is described earlier in this chapter).

He then turned to longitudinal balance, with particular reference to Langley's model experiments. However, because of his need to arrest his glider's forward motion by deliberately throwing his weight back before touchdown, Pilcher stated: "When a soaring machine is made to carry a man—automatic long[itudinal] balance cannot alone be relied on." "And," he added,

> the man must have it in his power to stop the machine from lifting him off the ground suddenly if a puff of wind comes if he does not wish it to do so—
>
> This could be done by fitting a horizontal rudder which the man could work—but much the easiest thing is for the man to move his weight about in the machine [perhaps a rather short-sighted rejection of the elevator owing to limited experience with small and light machines].

If he keeps his weight forward in a properly designed machine he will not lift if a puff of wind strikes the machine & if in the air he will descend—If he keeps his weight back a puff of wind will lift him off the ground—but if he keeps his weight too far back while in the air he will stop his forward motion & is liable to slip backwards in the air."

In discussing the wing area for flight and the resistance to forward motion that has to be overcome, Pilcher referred to Langley's experiments with flat planes. In retrospect, it is unfortunate that these important experiments with pressures on inclined planes, carried out between 1887 and 1891,[106] were not extended to include curved surfaces.

Langley's whirling-arm test rig could give only the most general results—there were far too many irregularities and inconsistencies to make his figures at all accurate.[107] But Pilcher described Lilienthal's apparatus for "similar experiments" as "much cruder." However, Lilienthal did test curved surfaces and thereby established that it required, in Pilcher's words, "very much less expenditure of energy to fly with curved wings than with flat." Even so, Langley, Lilienthal, and Pilcher were still in the dark ages of aerodynamics, and it was invariably by practice that the theories were finally proven or disproven. Nonetheless, it was clear that small angles of attack allowed the best lift with the minimum of drag, a fact that may seem obvious in these enlightened times, but was another new and vital piece of aerodynamic knowledge in the late 1880s.

Pilcher next outlined his estimation of the power needed "to drive air screws or flapping wings to convert a prac[tical] soaring machine into a prac[tical] flying machine." "As far as I can make out," he reasoned, "to drive soaring machines such as Herr Lils. or mine with a total weight of about 200 lbs. an Engine giving out about 2 HP would be required—I intend next summer to experiment with a machine of 170 sq. ft. surface carrying a 2 HP oil [petrol] engine which will drive 2 screws 1 under each wing—giving the machine a forward thrust of about 15 lbs.—at a speed of 30 miles per hour."

As he rightly pointed out, "many other considerations come into play," and with hindsight we can see that his estimate was hopelessly overoptimistic. The inefficiency of the engine, transmission, propeller, and wing curvature, combined with the drag of a heavily braced structure and the full frontal area of Pilcher's body, would have given the little power plant an impossible task. Nonetheless, the change from compressed carbonic acid gas to petrol is noteworthy.

In conclusion, Pilcher described his experiments that summer and autumn with the Bat, Beetle, and Gull, and his nearly complete but as yet unnamed 170-square-foot glider. He then showed some photographs received from Lilienthal only "a few days" earlier. These depicted the No. 13 and 14 gliders, Otto's first "doppeldeckers," or biplanes, which he had begun testing in September and October of 1895. Pilcher's experience with high-placed surfaces—the sharp dihedral of the original Bat and the uncontrollable Beetle—had made him extremely wary of multiplanes. "I do not consider this a safe machine," he commented.

In his covering letter, Lilienthal had expressed the wish that he and Pilcher "could join and get money" to further their work. Similar sentiments had come from Hiram Maxim, who had also written to Pilcher about the problems of setting up a large syndicate. Maxim's inconclusive experiments with his ambitious steam-powered machine from 1889 to 1894 had cost some £20,000.[108] Pilcher had achieved far more with humble bamboo hang gliders in six months, and at about 200th of the cost.

In the ensuing discussion[109] Sam Mavor, who was to record his memories of Pilcher in 1934, stated that he regretted "the apparent inclination of the gathering to treat the subject with levity," remarking that if the "soaring business" caught on it might hurt the popularity of golf. In reply, Percy pointed out that it was only since he had left Cardross that the place had taken to golf.

A Mr. Jackson suggested that a demonstration should be given at the college: "A descent from the Tower might be a good thing." Percy's response is not recorded.

In answer to Professor Barr's comment that a light motor was the great need, Percy said that there was a particularly light oil motor in America that weighed about 15 pounds and developed more than 4 horsepower. He hoped to obtain it for his trials of the next summer.

This engine was almost certainly the one developed by E. J. Pennington and produced by Thomas Kane and Company of Chicago, Illinois, and Racine, Wisconsin. Known as the Kane-Pennington motor, it was an extremely simple air-cooled two-cylinder engine with a 2½-inch bore and a 6-inch stroke. Gasoline or kerosene oil was gravity-fed into the cylinders, where it was vaporized and ignited by electric-spark ignition. In vaporizing, the fuel absorbed the heat from the previous explosion, thus providing a form of evaporative cooling. The engine had no water or water jacket, no carburetor, and no flywheel, and therefore weighed only 17½ pounds "all told," yet it was claimed to produce 4.75 horsepower at 700 revolutions per minute. It was fully described in the *Autocar*, a British magazine, in its issues for November 16 and December 7, 1895—shortly before Pilcher gave his lecture—and must have sounded ideal for aeronautical applications.[110] It later proved to be far from the miracle it seemed.

The day after his lecture, Pilcher penned a letter in reply to a gentleman who had written to the *Practical Engineer* under the pseudonym "Pneuma," querying the object of Percy's work. The correspondence continued for several issues, but Percy's letter of December 13 is particularly interesting:

> Sir,—In answer to "Pneuma" the object of my soaring experiments during last summer was to learn to balance a soaring machine, preparatory to adding a small engine and screw propellers. The advantages of learning in an apparatus without an engine are obvious: (1) It is lighter, (2) It is much less expensive, (3) It is less dangerous, and, I am glad to say, my experiments threw a good deal of light on some difficult points. As "Pneuma" says, I do not think that one could ever hope to maintain horizontal flight with a practical soaring machine to carry a man for more than a few seconds at a time, unless the machine was attached to the earth—at any rate, not in this country, where we cannot depend on upward currents of wind. I should have much more satisfaction in answering letters if the writers would sign their own names to them.
> Yours etc.
> University, Glasgow
> Dec. 13 1895[111] *Percy S. Pilcher*

As it transpired, the American motor was not to be purchased, and it would be some years before Pilcher was ready to fit an engine into a glider.

2

Pastures New, 1896

Work on the new glider occupied Pilcher well into the new year. Some time before February 20, while the work was still in progress, a letter arrived from Stanwell Park, Clifton, New South Wales, Australia. Its author was Lawrence Hargrave, a remarkable English-born inventor who had begun experimenting with heavier-than-air flying models and motors in 1882. Two years later he had tested some fifty rubber-powered models, convinced that flappers were the best means of propulsion. In 1889 Hargrave had designed and built the first rotary radial motor to be applied to aeronautical experiments, a small three-cylinder unit driven by compressed air. He invented the box kite in 1893, and in 1894, inspired by Lilienthal, he built a tandem-winged monoplane hang glider, but abandoned it after performing inconclusive tests in gusty conditions. The next year he designed a steam-powered, man-carrying box kite airplane.[1]

Hargrave's letter to Pilcher, dated December 11, 1895, read as follows:

> Dear Sir,
>
> A friend sent me a cutting from the "Scientific American Oct. 19, 1895" showing two of your soaring machines [the Bat and the Beetle]. I notice you are wrestling with piano-wire stayed surfaces, & I know the trouble of getting the fabric at the angle required, and keeping it there. Have you considered the relative merits of my cellular kites? The surfaces are not stayed, but strutted or boomed out, and are as rigid as the most exacting experimenter could desire. The large flying machine

Lawrence Hargrave (1850–1915), the Australian-domiciled pioneer, first wrote to Pilcher in late 1895. (Trustees of the Museum of Applied Arts and Sciences, Haymarket, New South Wales)

I am working on now, is to have only two cells with a total horizontal surface of 480 sq. ft. If you adopted this form for your apparatus the framing would assume the appearance sketched, and your surfaces would be [as] shown in red.

I send you my last pamphlet which will supply you with the detail of the booms, I am not sure if I sent it before, but if so, please pass it on to some one else.

If I may judge from the framing shown of your No. 2 [Beetle] I should say you have made it to stand rough usage: & strong enough to strike the ground without breaking. When I build any aeronautical things, I constantly keep in view that they are to be only strong enough to successfully withstand air pressure & that any but the lightest bump on the ground will fracture some part [Hargrave's underlining]. Suppose we had built our steamers with scantling to stand bumping on reefs, or climbing over sand banks, how could we ever have attained to their present development. Wishing you every success, believe me to be, yours truly.

Law. Hargrave[2]

Hargrave's sketch depicted a box kite hang glider with "side curtains" linking the upper and lower wing tips. The pilot hung with his forearms resting along the lower wing frame, and a "prism" of struts rose around him to the center of the top surface. To the apex of this prism was attached a boom that extended rearward to carry a high-set, smaller box kite tail.

Nearly a month was to pass before Pilcher answered this constructive and helpful letter. Hargrave was quite justified in pointing out the problems of maintaining a regular and rigid surface by the use of numerous bracing wires. Lilienthal had resolved this to some extent by fitting curved wooden "wing fences" chordwise across the top surface of his wings. These linked the radial ribs and did much to ensure that the required fore and aft camber was maintained.[3] Strangely, Pilcher never adopted this practice, but always preferred to rely entirely on extensive wire bracing. Perhaps his experience with ships' rigging during his naval service had endowed him with exceptional ability in this respect, or perhaps he was just a patient man.

On January 30, 1896, *Nature* magazine published an article by W. J. S. Lockyer on Lilienthal's experiments. Lockyer concluded with a reference to Pilcher's trials at Cardross, stating that they "have not as yet proved very successful."[4] This brought a quick response from Percy, who "did not consider this to be the case." In its issue for February 20, *Nature* published Pilcher's letter. In it, he outlines the progress made from the time he began construction of his first machine, "just a year ago," and describes the evolution of the Bat and its flights both free and under tow. Once again, he speaks of his plans to power a glider:

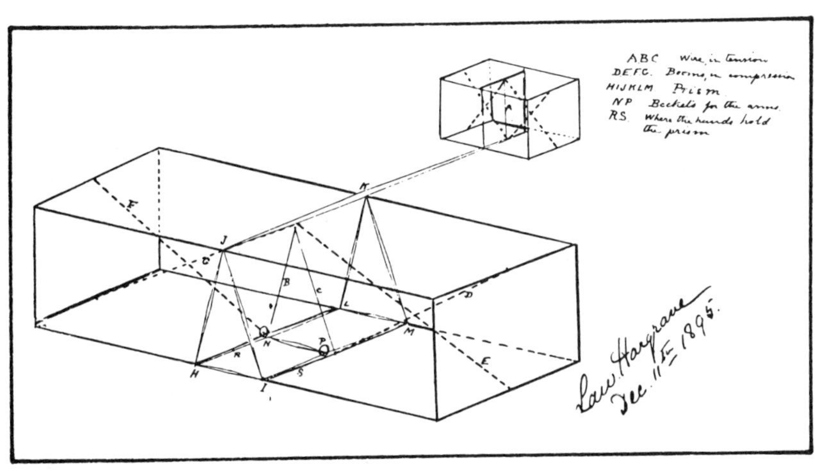

Lawrence Hargrave's suggestion for a box kite hang glider, from his letter to Pilcher dated December 11, 1895. (RAeS)

I had to stop experimenting at the end of September; but when I left off, I was pretty sure of my balance in the air, and was able to land without damage and without falling, even when soaring over the ground very fast. And this was the whole object of my work, so that I should be pretty sure of my balance before putting motive power into the machine to make horizontal flight possible. This I hope to do this year, with a petroleum engine, either working the screw propeller in front of the machine, or two screws, one placed under each wing, so that the machine will then practically become a Maxim machine of the smallest size possible for one man to fly with.

. . . I am confident that I could maintain horizontal flight with wings similar to those I have been using, or, better still, similar to those I am now making, which vary chiefly only in mechanical detail from the first, if driven forward as I propose.

Pilcher next referred to his visit to Lilienthal, adding that the German pioneer had "kept me informed of what he has been doing," and then mentioned Hargrave's letter. Commenting on Lilienthal's "double surface" machines, he said:

Although . . . a machine with the same area of sail can be made of less extreme dimensions, and a considerable saving can probably be made in weight, it has the disadvantage of having less area to act as a parachute in the event of speed through the air being lost, either by a sudden lull in the wind, or through want of skill on the part of the flyer. And I am as yet not at all sure that the upper surface with a puffy wind would not, from the very fact of its high position, prove a source of danger rather than the reverse.

My reason for saying this is because I tried a machine at Cardross with the wings just above my head [the Beetle], but found the machine with the low wings [the modified Bat] very much more easy to handle, especially when the wind was puffy; but in order to make sure of this, I shall probably make a double surface machine at once.

It is quite possible that what is best at Herr Lilienthal's ideal practising place, where he has his cone-shaped hill and flat country for miles round, so that his wind is unbroken and steady, is not best in the proverbially squally district of the Clyde, where I have had to experiment.[5]

Despite his expressed intention to build a multiplane right away, it was to be some time before he would do so. The reference to his

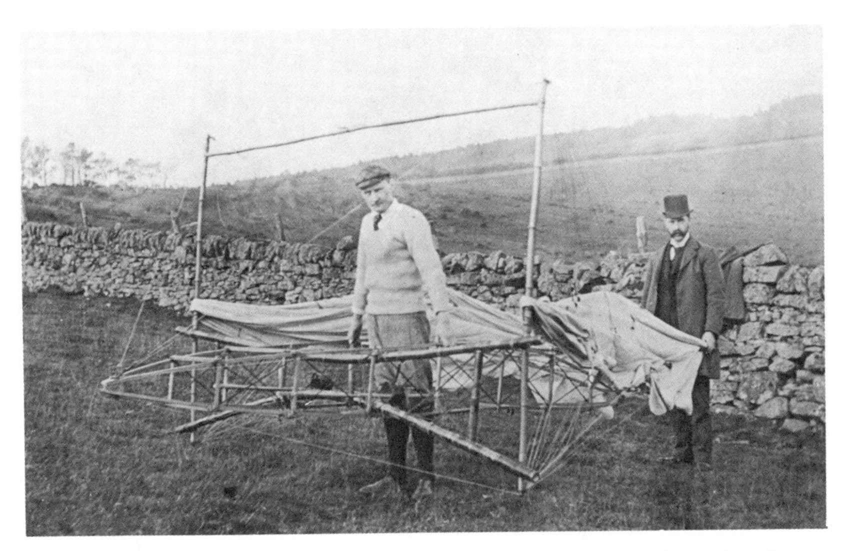

Pilcher and an assistant demonstrate the way to carry the Gull. "Moving the machine from one field to the other, over hedges, ditches, gates &c" was a problem. (RAeS)

This study of Percy with the Gull clearly shows the new bracing system, with two widely spaced kingposts, now linked by a crossbar. Also visible on the nose of the glider is a vertical stick with a piece of string blowing in the wind at its top—the first slip indicator. (RAeS)

A three-quarter rear view of the Gull emphasizes the great wing area—300 square feet—which was its downfall. (Author)

projected powered machine being of the "Maxim" type revealed an influence that was soon to lure Pilcher away from Glasgow.

Further trials of the Gull were probably made in the early months of 1896. Photographs of the glider that seem to have been taken about this time show that a crossbar had been added between the kingpost tops, and one picture reveals that Percy was using the first flight instrument. A vertical stick is fitted on the nose of the Gull, and tied to its top is a piece of string that served as a slip indicator, or helped Pilcher to ensure that his glider was pointed into wind before take-off—possibly the earliest application of this simple but valuable device.

On March 16, writing from the university, Pilcher penned his reply to Hargrave. They had evidently communicated previously, as Pilcher already had the pamphlet and had sent a copy of the *Glasgow Evening Citizen* of October 19, 1895, in return; however, Hargrave had not received it.[6] Pilcher wrote:

> I am thinking of making either a machine such as you suggest (i.e. cellular), or else some other type of double surface one. I am rather afraid of the vertical surfaces in the front of the machine [the "side curtains"], as in a puff it [*sic*] might have the tendency to make the machine pay off from the wind—our winds here are extremely puffy—I am exceedingly anxious to put an oil engine & screw propeller into one

of my machines this summer—and I think that if I did so I could balance with the practice I have had—

I have just finished my No. 4 machine of which I will try & remember to send you particulars as soon as anything is published—It has wheels with springs [for] landing on & weighs 50lbs. all told 170 sq. ft. surface—nearly all bamboo—[7]

As this letter suggests, Pilcher's failure to build a biplane may have been due to an inability to decide whether to make it of the Lilienthal or Hargrave type.

Percy's newly completed glider inherited many features from its immediate predecessor, the Gull, although it had much less wing area. For example, its monoplane wings were made so that they could be folded back alongside the body. Each had nine radial bamboo ribs, all but two of which were stayed by six piano-wire braces, three to the top of their respective bamboo kingpost, and three to the bottom. The two shorter ribs, which supported the wing leading edge, had only four wires apiece. In all, there were 100 bracing wires to support and shape the wing structure. Further wires ran from the nose of the glider to the top and bottom of the kingposts, and hemp lines ran to the fin and tailplane from the upper kingpost extensions only; wires from the wing trailing-edge rib ends stiffened the tail laterally. Fabric sleeves stitched to the wing undersurface were used to hold the fabric to the ribs, reinforced holes being provided in the wing surface to allow the bracing wire to pass through. A wooden plug with a loop of iron wire lashed to its end was inserted in the root end of each rib. This loop fitted around the kingpost, thereby enabling the rib to pivot around it.

Each bracing wire ended in a curtain ring, and this was linked, by several turns of a length of string or twine (as on the final Bat variant), to an eye bound onto the rib, or, at the extremities of the rib, to an eyelet let into the hollow end of the bamboo. The curtain ring at the other end of the bracing wire passed over the head of a large screw fixed into the top or bottom end of the kingpost.

A beam linking the tops of these kingposts was held to them by metal brackets that passed around the kingposts and were screwed into the beam. The main beam beneath the wings was also held between the kingposts by wraparound metal brackets screwed into place.

The "fuselage" comprised two bows of bamboo held together at the front and rear by cast metal sockets that also carried bracing points. The rearmost casting also incorporated the fitting for the tail

With the Glasgow tenements as a backdrop, Pilcher displays his newly completed fourth glider, later to be named Hawk. The deep camber of the wings is evident in this picture, which was probably taken in March 1896. (Author)

Percy lifts the wings of the Hawk on the grounds of Glasgow University to reveal undersurface detail. Note the hinged tail boom and the fact that the fabric is attached above the ribs. Ella stands alongside. (Author)

boom, which was held by a pin passing through an end fitting that mated into the casting. The tailplane was formed of a triangle made of three lengths of bamboo and fabric stretched across them; an extra bamboo "leading edge" member was fitted. In a marked departure from previous practice, Pilcher had decided not to fit any fin at all, to see if any advantage could be gained by omitting it.[8] The old circular surfaces were abandoned, and instead of hinging the tailplane to the fin at its leading edge, he hinged the whole boom and tailplane—upward only—at the rear of the body. Thus the tail surface could still "give" when the machine was tipped up for landing; moreover, the tail boom was unlikely to be broken if it struck the ground. The pilot slipped his forearms through a pair of padded sleeves in the frame and grasped two small struts.

The most conspicuous addition to the machine was an undercarriage. The legs were held to the main beam by wide leather straps and lashing, and inside the hollow bamboo upper part were "very stiff spiral springs." Thinner lower struts with turned wooden wheels attached to their ends slid up against the springs inside the upper members, thus providing a comfortable degree of shock absorption for the vertical jar of a heavy touchdown. A metal rod linked each wheel axle to its appropriate kingpost, to which it was attached by a metal fitting. Although the surviving drawing suggests that the wheels were to have rubber tires, this does not seem to have been the case.

The fabric wing covering was drawn tight by tape loops with string "adjusters" that were tied to the eyes in the rib ends. Strengthening patches were sewn around all holes and at tape attachment points. All bamboo members were carefully whipped to minimize the risk of their splitting.

Pilcher apparently braced the wings so that they had an almost "umbrella-like" camber, which was at its maximum (5 inches) at the pivot point around the kingposts, 2 feet 6 inches behind the leading edge. The wing span was 24 feet 8 inches, and the chord was 10 feet. The glider's overall length was 18 feet 6 inches.

Despite the addition of the undercarriage, Pilcher had contrived to keep the new machine's empty weight down to only 50 pounds; thus the wing loading was a little over 1 pound per square foot. Doubtless the extensive use of bamboo had helped to make this low loading possible.

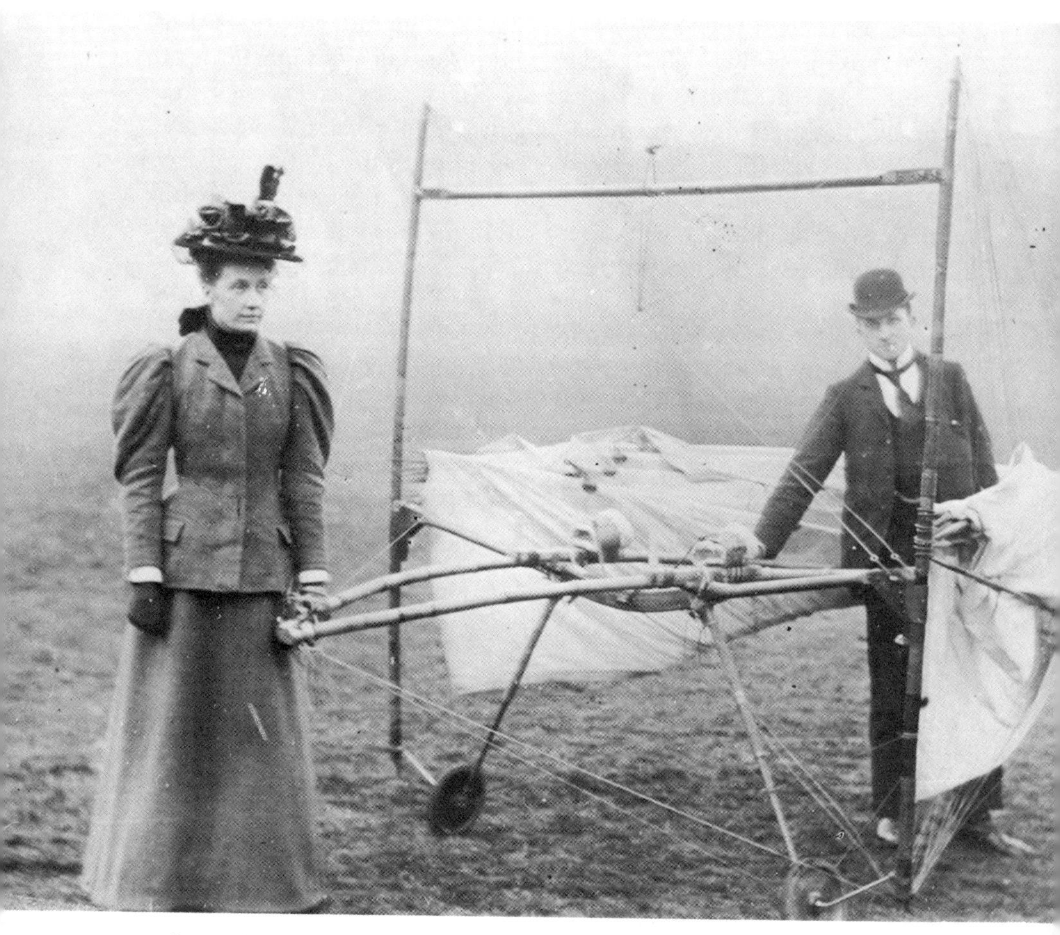

The Hawk folded for transport, with Ella and an assistant alongside. The sprung wheeled undercarriage is shown here, but the tail boom has been removed. (Author)

Although the new glider's structure was basic, the workmanship was of a high standard, and compared favorably with that of Lilienthal's machines.

That Percy held out great hopes for his latest creation is beyond doubt, for he made it the subject of a British patent concerning "Improvements in Flying and Soaring Machines." This patent, no. 9144 of 1896, was Pilcher's only aircraft patent. It was applied for on April 30, 1896, the complete specification was left on January 22, 1897, and it was accepted on March 6, 1897.[9]

Although it described the general construction of the glider and the means of installing an engine, it referred "particularly to the means for keeping the wings rigid and for enabling them to be folded up, and to the means for supporting the aeronaut in or on the said machines." (The patent is reproduced in full in appendix B.)

The aircraft described was the new glider in its earliest form, without a fin, and with only sleeves for the "aeronaut's" forearms. The framework of the body and wings was to be made of bamboo, wood, or even steel tube; the wing covering could be closely woven cotton or some other similar material, "but gold-beaters' skin may be used." The method of attaching the fabric to the wings and the means of furling the wings for storage and transportation were detailed. The reason for the fore and aft curvature of the wings was explained thus: "At small angles to the wind the lifting power is greater for the same resistance to forward motion, and the longitudinal balance can be more easily controlled for the longitudinal shift of the centre of lift is less in the case of a suitably curved surface than it is in the case of a plane or flat surface."

Pilcher stated that it was preferable to have only a horizontal tail surface, "but it may have a vertical surface or blade also." In all of his writings he consistently refers to these fixed surfaces as "rudders." This is misleading, as the term *rudder* denotes a movable control surface operated by the pilot. In fact, he used only fixed tailplane and fin surfaces.

In describing his engine installation, Pilcher specified an "oil [petrol], spirit, or other engine" and offered several drive systems (in accordance with the normal practice of couching a patent in broad terms to allow for as many variations of the basic idea as possible). His preferred layout had the engine mounted above the front of the body piece, with a long driveshaft running back above the pilot's head to turn a two-bladed, fan-type pusher propeller behind him. "Or," the patent reads,

> the engine may be behind and the propeller in front or there may be two propellers, one under each wing connected for instance to the motor by shafting and bevel gearing or in any other convenient manner. Or if convenient the engine and the propeller may be in close proximity. Although I have shown the engine and the propeller with their axes in the same plane, this is not essential as the axes may be in differ-

ent planes and motion may be transmitted from the engine as aforesaid by means of bevel or other gearing.

The fall from favor of the "Maxim-type" installation with a propeller beneath each wing is noteworthy. It was the result of Pilcher's concern that the propeller should not be positioned where it could be easily "injured," as he made clear at an Aeronautical Society of Great Britain meeting in December 1897.[10] The newly proposed layout, with its extraordinarily long driveshaft, seems equally cumbersome to modern eyes, but it was to remain in favor to the end.

The strength of the link between Pilcher and Hiram Maxim up to this point is not clear. A leaflet printed in 1896 stated that "Mr. Pilcher has for a long time been acting as Mr. Maxim's assistant in his aeronautical experiments, and is now acting as his chief assistant."[11] It is, of course, quite possible that he acted in an advisory capacity while still employed by the university. However, it is certain that correspondence had passed between them, even if they had not met, as Pilcher had referred to some of Maxim's experiments, and to a letter received from Maxim, in his lecture at the end of 1895. Moreover, although Pilcher had proved his ability to design and build light practical gliders, he seemed to lack the heavy engineering experience and skills needed to produce an engine. To some degree, therefore, the skills of Maxim and Pilcher were complementary, although their respective approaches to powered flight differed greatly. In the 1890s, however, all who evinced an interest in heavier-than-air flight were joined by the common bond of enthusiasm for what was generally regarded as a singularly "eccentric" subject. Although quite a number of these enthusiasts exchanged long and passionate letters in scientific journals, those who actually pursued a practical line of experiment were relatively few, and, like the members of any minority group, they intermixed.

Consequently, it is not at all surprising that Britain's two foremost aeronautical experimenters at the time, Pilcher and Maxim, should work together. At some time between mid-March and mid-April 1896, Percy resigned his post at Glasgow University and went south to work as Maxim's "assistant" in the Maxim Nordenfeld Guns and Ammunition Co. Ltd., presumably at the latter's invitation. He moved into accommodations in Artillery Mansions, Victoria Street, London.[12]

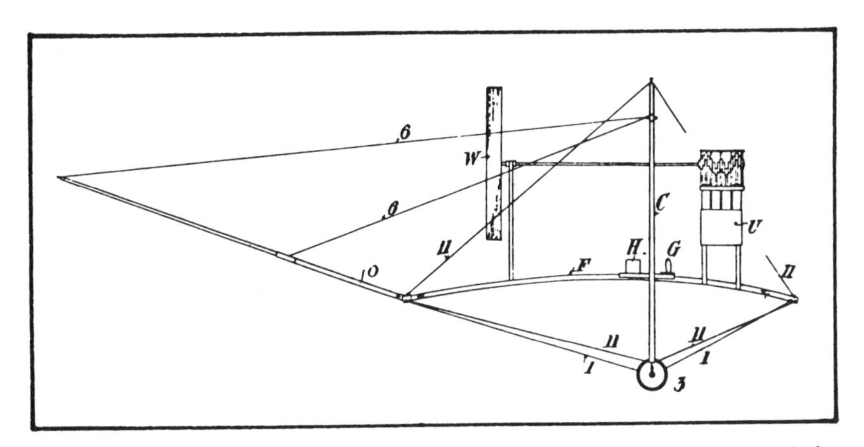

A side elevation from Pilcher's patent of 1896, No. 9144, showing the proposed method of installing an engine, with a long driveshaft passing over the pilot's head to a pusher propeller behind him. (Controller of Her Majesty's Stationery Office)

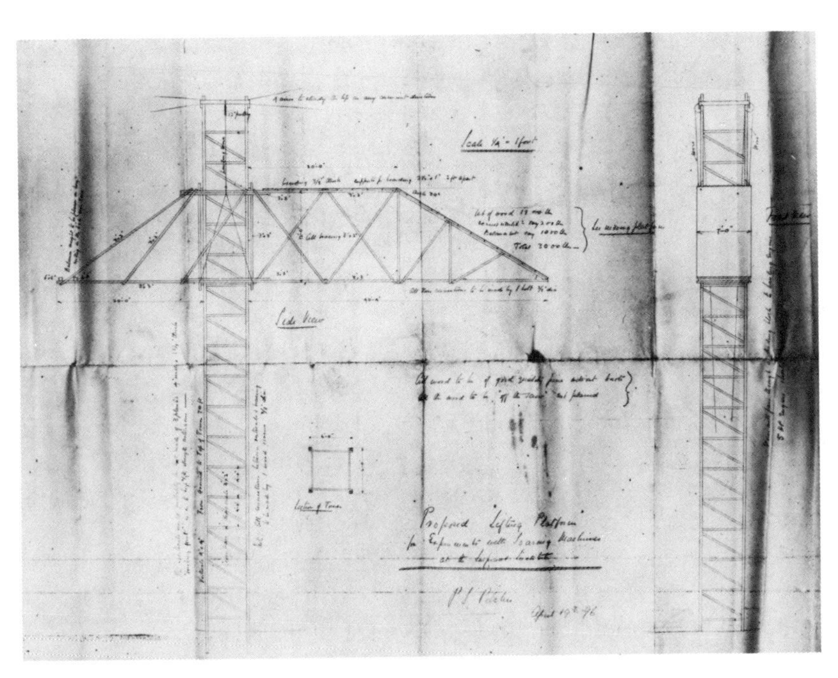

Pilcher's drawing, dated April 19, 1896, for a "Lifting Platform" to be erected at the Imperial Institute for gliding demonstrations. It was not built. (Trustees of the Science Museum, London)

The Maxim Nordenfeld company was the result of the amalgamation in 1888 of the Maxim Gun Co. Ltd., formed in 1884 to market Maxim's machine gun, and the Nordenfeld Guns and Ammunition Co. Ltd., formed in 1886 to exploit the patents of Swedish engineer Thorsten Nordenfeld. The Maxim company's works were at Crayford in Kent, and the Nordenfeld factory was a few miles to the northeast, at Erith. Automatic and quick-firing guns were tested at "Eynsford Ranges," located on Upper Austin Lodge Farm, to the south of Eynsford.[13]

Maxim had been forced to discontinue experiments with his massive biplane in 1894, first by the lack of funds and second by eviction from his test site at Baldwyn's Park to make way for an asylum.[14] As he maintained "effective managerial supervision"[15] over the Maxim Nordenfeld company, it must have been easy for him to obtain leave to reerect his purpose-built Baldwyn's Park hangar at Upper Austin Lodge, on the east side of and separated from the ranges by a large hill now known as "The Knob." Into this enormous building—one of the world's first airplane hangars—was moved Pilcher's diminutive new and untried glider, and also, probably, the larger Gull. It seems that the Bat and Beetle were left in Scotland.[16]

The two experimenters immediately began to prepare for an "International Exhibition of Motors and Their Appliances" at London's Imperial Institute, in South Kensington. Pilcher seems to have had ambitious plans for this event, for on April 19 he completed a two-view general arrangement drawing of a "Proposed 'Lifting Platform' for Experiments with Soaring Machines at the Imperial Institute." This drawing, signed by Pilcher, survives in the library of the Royal Aeronautical Society.[17] It shows a 70-foot-high square-section wooden tower joined by wood screws and stayed by four wires from its top corners. Riding up the tower is a "moving platform" comprising a bolted open wooden girder structure that is 7 feet wide and 12 feet deep and is supported by two "hauling wires." These wires pass over two 12-inch-diameter pulleys at the top of the tower and run back down "through a leading block" to the "hauling" motor—"5 h.p. engine should be quite sufficient," notes Pilcher.

The overall length of the moving platform is 66 feet 4 inches, of which 40 feet 4 inches projects forward (its top is covered with 3/8-inch boarding); the projection runs straight out for 20 feet and then drops at 30 degrees to the bottom beams to provide a "run up" and a sloping ramp. The structure also extends rearward 20 feet and can carry counterbalance weights at its extreme end. The whole lifting platform is rather reminiscent of the cranes seen on modern building sites, though it is much smaller and built of wood "good quality pine without knots" is specified, " 'off the saw,' not planed." Pilcher estimated the total weight of the tower to be 3,000 pounds.

It was obviously intended that the experimenter, carrying his "wings," would climb up the slope onto the level boards of the platform and turn with his back to the tower. The platform would then be raised to the desired height by the engine-driven pulley system; the experimenter would run along the platform, down the 30-degree slope, and glide to earth.

Following a reception and "inaugurating Banquet" on Friday May 1, to celebrate the "first International Motor Carriage Exhibition held in England," the exhibition was formally opened by His Royal Highness the Prince of Wales on Saturday May 9, the opening day of the summer season at the Imperial Institute. The exhibition was run by the Motor Car Club Syndicate and comprised no fewer than fifteen sections covering all aspects of "self-propelled traffic," from "motor pleasure carriages" to road maps and camping equipment.[18]

The exhibition was installed in the North Gallery (United Kingdom Section) of the Imperial Institute and the special gallery in the East Quadrangle.[19] Practical demonstrations were to take place daily in the West Quadrangle, part of which had been "converted into a track with gradients on which to test the various machines."[20] "The celebrated Monte Carlo band [Orchestra]," proclaimed the Motor Car Club's vice-president, Frederick R. Simms, "will play for the first time this season in the newly-decorated and magnificent gardens of the Imperial Institute."[21] It was also announced that "valuable monetary prizes to the amount of £1,000 are to be given for new designs and inventions. Eminent engineers and experts will adjudicate upon the merits of the respective exhibits."[22]

Section 6 of the exhibition was devoted to "Apparatus for Aerial Navigation through the agency of motors." On view were a one-twelfth-scale wooden model of Maxim's flying machine, one of the two 180-horsepower compound steam engines from the aircraft, and its starboard screw propeller, which was 17 feet 10 inches in diameter. Also shown was the dynamometer and slip rope used to measure the horizontal pull (thrust) of the machine. Major Moore provided one of

his flying machines, with wings based on those of the flying fox, and a Mr. H. Middleton of Slough showed "a balloon flying machine and other aerial models."[23]

Also on display was the Lilienthal No. 11 glider owned by T. J. Bennett of Oxford, who had purchased it from Lilienthal in the spring of 1895 for £25. The *Autocar* commented, "The 'Glider', we suppose, can lay some claim to be termed a horseless carriage, and that, we presume, is sufficient reason for its finding a place here." "Hard by" the Maxim exhibit was Pilcher's new glider. "Mr. Pilcher . . . is present," reported the *Autocar,* "and willingly gives any earnest person full details of his experiences."[24] In a handbill put out by Maxim and Pilcher, it was requested that all communications regarding their exhibits be addressed to Pilcher at Maxim's "Experimental Department," 32, Victoria Street, London SW.[25]

The exhibition lasted through May, June, July, and August and thus prevented Percy from making any trials with his new glider for some time. Reports make no reference whatsoever to Pilcher's proposed Lifting Platform, so it seems that common sense—and the fact that the institute's gardens were newly decorated—had ruled it out. Perhaps this was fortunate, for there was no provision for it to be pointed into wind, there would have been no rising air currents of the kind found on natural slopes, and the airflow in the vicinity of the institute must have been far from smooth.

Doubtless, Maxim was keeping his new assistant busy. Nonetheless, Pilcher found time to visit Lilienthal again when he "happened" to make a trip to Berlin in June.[26] He obviously expressed his mistrust of multiplanes to Lilienthal, for he later reported that "Herr Lilienthal kindly allowed me to sail down his hill in one of these double surface machines"[27] in "a light steady breeze."[28] The German's object in making them, Percy stated, "was to get more surface without increasing the length and width of the machine." Although he found that, "with the great facility afforded by his [Lilienthal's] conical hill the machine was handy enough," Pilcher remained doubtful of the biplane's safety: "I personally strongly object to any machine in which the wing surface is high above the weight. I consider that it makes the

Otto Lilienthal flies his No. 13 biplane glider at Gollenberg in 1896. Pilcher was extremely wary of wing surfaces positioned high above the pilot. (Smithsonian Institution)

machine very difficult to handle in bad weather, as a puff of wind striking the surface, high above one, has a great tendency to heel the machine over." He added, "I am afraid I should not be able to manage one at all in the squally districts I have had to practice in over here."[29] Old prejudices—particularly those born of personal experience—die hard.

Probably during mid- to late June, Percy received another letter from Lawrence Hargrave in Australia, written on April 24. Hargrave was still anxious to convince Pilcher of the value of inherent stability by use of his box kite principle:

> I think if you make a small cellular kite just to try its stability in gusty weather you will find how the vertical surfaces act.
>
> Perhaps it will assist you if I make a diagram: starting with the axiom that a perfectly flat surfaced kite cannot possibly fly: a kite must have diehedral [*sic*] angle or its equivalent: your own machines have it.
>
> Let

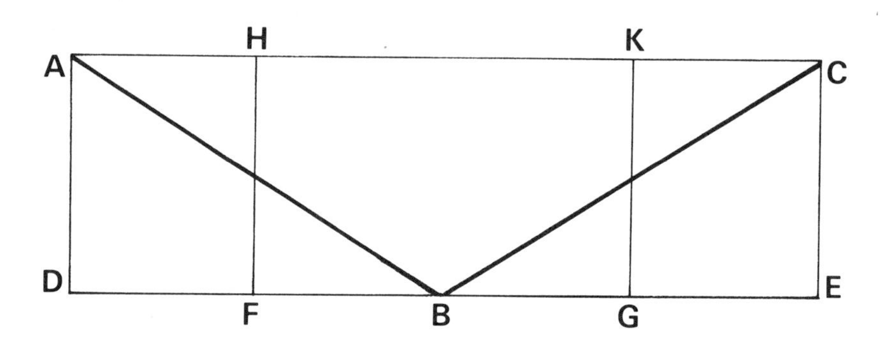

> Let ABC be the dihedral angle B being the end view of the back bone. Resolve AB & BC into their components: DBE is the breadth of surface that tends to lift the kite. AD & CE are the heights of the surfaces that tend to steady the kite: Bisect DB & BE & erect perpendiculars FH & GK. FHGK is the breadth & height of a cell having the same lifting power as ABC & (apparently) greater stability.
>
> You see I halve the spread [span] and thereby show an equal area with much less timbering.
>
> I am working away at steam boilers but think you will easily outstrip me with an oil engine. I have not got any detail of the latest oil motors but such information as I have leads me to think they will suit small flying machines.[30]

When he wrote this letter, Hargrave was obviously unaware of the Gull and the new glider, in which the dihedral angle was virtually eliminated.

Pilcher's reply, written from Maxim's Victoria Street address on June 25, reveals the difference of opinion that was opening up between the theorists, kite flyers, and model makers and those who had flown in full-size hang gliders:

> We are rather at cross purposes. With your kites you naturally aim at stability, but with my soaring machines, stability, strange as it may appear, is a thing that I am very much afraid of. I like to have the machines practically neutral so as to be perfectly under control, or rather, more susceptible to the control movements of my body. For instance, if a soaring machine is stable transversely, either by having the wings at a dihedral angle, or by having the wing surface considerably raised above the centre of weight, although stable and stiff with the wind coming directly from ahead, if the wind shifts ever so little to the one side it must necessarily have a capsizing tendency, and this capsizing tendency will vary directly, and not inversely, as the transverse stability.
>
> In my first machine . . . the wing tips were considerably raised and so the machine had transverse stability, but I had to lower the wings tips [*sic*] so that they were practically at the same level as the centre because I kept on getting overturned by puffs of wind from unexpected directions. Of course this would not be the case if one were far in the air, one would have time to recover but when standing on the ground a machine which is stiff sideways will always get capsized by a change in the direction of wind.
>
> During the winter I made a new machine . . . and it has wheels and springs for taking a jar on alighting. To this machine I hope shortly to be able to add, with Mr. Maxim's help, a small oil engine and a screw propeller, then starting from an eminence I shall be able to make attempts at horizontal flight. You may possibly have seen in the papers that Mr. Maxim is thinking about making another flying machine but about this I will write to you when there is something more definite to tell you.
>
> I wish you would point out in some of the newspapers that what Professor Langley has done, and about which there has been so much talk, is practically no more than you yourself have done years ago.[31]

The reference to "attempts at horizontal flight" is significant, for it clearly shows that Pilcher was aiming at producing a "powered glider" as an intermediate step toward a "fully powered" airplane.

The allusion to the machine that Maxim was "thinking about" almost certainly refers to the large twin-rotored helicopter granted British Patent No. 10,620 in April 1897 and accepted on April 2, 1898. This machine had a pair of four-bladed rotors mounted side by side and tilted slightly forward. "Steering" could be exercised either by applying differential rotational speeds to the rotors or by varying their pitch, but a rudder was preferred. Provision was also made for the use of small auxiliary screws at the front and rear of the machine that could be rotated through 180 degrees while they were in motion to direct their thrust as a lifting or propelling force. Two four-cylinder engines powered by acetylene gas were to provide the power.[32]

Percy's parting reference to "what Professor Langley has done" referred to the events of May 6, when two successful launches and flights of the professor's model "Aerodrome No. 5" (Langley dubbed all his airplanes "Aerodrome" owing to a mistranslation from the Greek) were made from a houseboat on the Potomac River. On its first flight, the 3-pound, 4-meter span, tandem-winged machine, powered by a 1-horsepower steam engine driving two pusher propellers, covered an estimated 3,300 feet in three circles at a speed of 20–25 miles per hour. The second flight followed a similar pattern but covered some 2,300 feet. It was the "first time a large flying model with a self-contained power plant had remained in the air for a length of time sufficient to demonstrate that it had unquestionably flown."[33] Pilcher's comment was not really justified. For all their ingenuity, Hargrave's models, somewhat smaller than Langley's and usually powered by compressed air engines driving flappers, never approached the performance of the successful model "Aerodromes."[34]

In July the adjudication of the Imperial Institute exhibits took place. Maxim was one of the four judges, the other three being Professor Donkin, Professor Beare and Mr. Beaumont, editor of *The Engineer.* As it turned out, only Maxim and Donkin carried out the adjudication, and they decided to postpone awarding the £1,000 because "it was practically impossible to form a fair and reliable opinion as to the merits of the motor carriages offered for competition in the space available at the Institute."[35]

Early in August tragic news came from Germany. On Sunday August 9, while gliding from the Gollenberg, near Stölln, in one of his standard No. 11 monoplanes, Lilienthal was suddenly gusted to a standstill in midair. Although he threw his weight as far forward as possible to bring the glider's nose down, the machine stalled, dropped its starboard wing and side-slipped into the ground, crumpling up the starboard wing. Otto broke his spine in the crash, and he was taken to the Bergmann Clinic in Berlin the following day. Unfortunately an operation was out of the question, and the great German pioneer of aviation died that same day.[36]

Many inventors with pet theories on the best means of flying submitted letters to the press, pointing out where Lilienthal had obviously erred and stating in their infinite wisdom how it should be done. One such letter, from Douglas Archibald, a fellow and past president of the Royal Meteorological Society, was published in the *Saturday Review.*[37] Mr. Archibald, who had visited Hargrave early in the year, again argued for an inherently stable machine, citing Hargrave's box kite as the prime example of a stable device. He evinced familiarity with Hargrave's then-current project for a powered man-carrying aircraft—his second—which was to be a box kite biplane with a steam engine driving four flappers. "In order to convert such an aeroplane into a flying machine," writes Archibald, "Mr. Hargrave is adding moveable front and rear planes by which the inclination can be altered, as well as side planes to partially imitate the adjusting wing movements employed by soaring and sailing birds." Despite this tantalizing description of the control system, the crude surviving sketch of this project shows its only control to be a small cruciform surface acting as an elevator-cum-rudder. The machine was to be float-mounted for free takeoffs from water. In the event, its engine proved a failure and the aircraft was not built.[38]

"The lesson to be learnt from the fate of Lilienthal," continued Archibald, "is that, in the absence of power sufficient to make rapid side wing movements [he had proposed motor-driven 'auxiliary wing movements'], man must primarily use a double aeroplane with closed-in vertical sides. . . . Lilienthal's unfortunate accident merely points out a weakness against which Mr. Hargrave has fortunately provided."

Archibald attributed Lilienthal's accident "to the fact that his aeroplane was fundamentally unstable," and implied that it was its lateral instability that had led to his death. This brought a smart response from Pilcher, dated August 28 and published in the *Saturday Review* for September 5.[39] Pilcher was under the impression that

Lilienthal had been using a new head-harness elevator control at the time of the mishap. This is now known to be incorrect: he was flying a standard No. 11 monoplane built in 1895.[40] Pilcher's account, possibly culled from press and eyewitness reports, states:

> His accident had nothing to do with transverse stability: he pitched endways. Having started from a high hill and made an excellent soar, in which he had lost only very little in elevation, he lost his forward speed through the air; partly, it appears, from the accounts of onlookers, through having ridden his machine with his weight rather far back, in order that he might gain full benefit from an anticipated puff of wind, and partly because, from a sudden lull in the wind he found himself all at once without motion through the air. He consequently put his weight forward to incline the front of the machine downwards, that he might regain his forward speed; but unfortunately he tilted the machine too much down in front and descended practically end on.

The damage to the starboard wing, visible in a picture of the wreckage,[41] suggests that a wing drop following the stall was probably the case, rather than a nose-over into a vertical dive. Whatever the case, the result was the same. Percy's inspirer and mentor was gone.

Yet again Percy argued for instability:

> It is a matter of experience, both Herr Lilienthal's and my own, that if a machine is made stable sideways it will constantly come to grief . . . by making the machine quite neutral transversely, which can be effected by making the wing tips only very slightly raised above the centre of the machine and by making the wings hollow [arched] transversely, the machine can be handled comparatively easily in a shifting wind, the transverse balance being maintained by throwing the weight of the body from side to side.

Archibald replied in the issue of September 12,[42] blaming inaccurate press reports for his misinterpretation of the accident, but defending his case for automatic stability, restressing his faith in the box kite principle. Pilcher did not bother to respond a second time.

Lilienthal's death also resulted in the publication of a long article by W. E. Garret Fisher in the *Glasgow Herald*[43] pointing out that Lilienthal was considering the possibility of true soaring flight shortly before his death:

Sometimes the wind also lifted him high above his starting point, and this seems to have made him see the possibility of imitating the flight of many birds, which rise by soaring in circles, and then advance by a long sloping descent.

One of his latest utterances states that this action of the wind occasionally brought him to a standstill in the air. "At these times," he said, "I feel very certain that if I leaned a little to one side and so described a circle, and further partook of the motion of the rising air around me, I should sustain my position. The wind itself tends to direct this motion; but then it must be remembered that my chief object in the air is to overcome this tendency to turn to the right or left, because I know that behind and under me lies the hill from which I have started, and with which I should come in rough contact if I allowed myself to attempt this circle sailing. I have, however, made up my mind, either by means of a stronger wind or by flapping the wings, to get higher up and further away from the hills, so that, sailing round in circles, I can follow the strong uplifting currents, and have sufficient air space under and about me safely to complete a circle, and, lastly, to come down again against the wind to earth."

It seems quite possible that Lilienthal had decided to fly from the Gollenberg, rather than from his man-made hill, so that he might attempt this maneuver. On the natural slopes he would certainly have got the "stronger wind" that he desired. As Fisher comments: "Herr Lilienthal's success in flying, say, a dozen miles by this compound soaring and gliding movement would not, indeed, have opened the air to all of us, but it would have shown the way of success to the athlete, and introduced him to a new and fascinating, even if dangerous, sport."

In a concluding allusion to Pilcher's work, Fisher revealed that he was unaware that the Englishman had moved his experiments from Glasgow to Kent. His final sentence, however, deserves quoting for its entertainment value alone: "One trusts that his own experiments . . . will prove more successful, and that at no distant date Glasgow may be convulsed by the appearance of a veritable flying man hovering high above the Municipal Buildings, and gracefully alighting in George Square, with the empire of the air at last securely within his grasp."

It is worth pointing out that Pilcher, unlike Lilienthal, never talks of circular soaring flights. In fact, while Lilienthal had at times risen higher than his point of takeoff, Pilcher was never to achieve even that satisfaction.

Although his mentor's death underlined the great risks that he was taking, Pilcher pressed ahead with his own experiments at Upper Austin Lodge. During 1896 he flew both the Gull and his new, finless machine. Of the Gull he stated in January 1897 that he "got it broken up twice last year, and have not yet had time to rebuild it. It was intended for practice only on calm days; but I had not patience to wait for them, and took it out when there was practically no holding the large wing surface."[44] It seems reasonable to speculate that, while the new glider was on show in the Imperial Institute for four months, Pilcher was left with only the Gull to fly. His frustration at having to wait for calm weather can be imagined.

However, he did eventually manage to try his new machine "during the latter part of [the] Summer," when he had it out "about ten times" at Eynsford. "I have unfortunately had to be very busy about other things," he reported, "and have not been able to spend much time in experimenting."[45] A letter from Percy to an unidentified gentleman, dated November 24, contains a brief reference to flights made on Saturday and Sunday, November 21 and 22, "to get some new photos for slides" (for a forthcoming lecture). "On Sunday," he writes, "I cleared 80 yards in a calm—& I believe I went *up* hill thus." A simple accompanying sketch traces the glider's path down a slope, rising briefly to clear a "big bush I was frightened of coming into."[46] As he makes so much of the achievement, we can be fairly certain that this was the first time that he had actually gained any height at all. Following a lecture to the Glasgow University Engineering Society on the night of January 28, 1897,[47] Pilcher enlarged on the circumstances of this flight. The *Glasgow Evening Citizen* for the next day reported: "He said he had made quite a nice jump in the air the other day. He was flying down a steep hill, and the machine was making for a big bush. He had smashed it on bushes the day before, so he got back in the machine slightly and shot over the bush, and down again on the other side."[48]

By the end of these few flights, the new glider was somewhat the worse for wear. "Please remember," he stated in January 1897,

> this machine has been drenched several times, and several times I have landed in bushes, and once caught in a wire fence while going fast, and so does not look so fresh as when she was first built.

The finless Hawk outside Maxim's enormous hangar at Upper Austin Lodge Farm, Eynsford, Kent, in 1896. The disposition of the fabric rib sleeves and the strengthening patches is well shown. (Trustees of the Science Museum, London)

> . . . The greatest distance I have cleared with this machine is about 100 yards—once with a slight sidewind, once in a dead calm. Most unfortunately I have never had the machine out when it has been blowing up the best hill for experimenting at Eynsford, or I should be able to record much longer distances.[49]

On Monday November 30, 1896, Dr. (later Prof.) G. H. Bryan—who was to receive the Gold Medal of the Aeronautical Society of Great Britain in 1914 for his development of the theory of the stability of airplanes—gave a lecture at the Imperial Institute on "Flight, Natural and Artificial."[50] Pilcher assisted the lecturer, and his new glider was suspended over the audience. During the proceedings it was lowered, and its designer explained its operation and demonstrated his technique. At the end of Bryan's lecture, Pilcher proposed the vote of thanks, and his notes for this, written on paper headed "Experimental Department of Hiram S. Maxim," have survived.[51] His words evince dedication, unselfishness, and a realistic vision of the task ahead:

> We can hardly hope that any one series of experiments will stand out as the land mark showing the way to complete success, but each set of carefully thought out and well conducted trials will in all probability show up at least some one fatal error, into which others would fall, and so by the regular recording of the wreckages of the first enthusiast, a channel is being gradually buoyed out which already leads us to the means of obtaining results which would have been impossible by first attempts.
>
> We must not each work only for our own selfish interests but all have at heart the common cause. And if only this is done and those who can spare money will risk a little in the hands of those who by their special training should be best qualified to conduct the search, the rest of the way to true flight will soon be marked out; not by any one great invention but by the careful compiling of quantitative data and the elimination of errors and fallacies.
>
> We now no longer grope in such utter blindness for the first essential experimental truths as the earlier experimenters but there is a very great deal of which we still remain hopelessly ignorant.
>
> I should like for my own part to thank Dr. Bryan for having given a lecture which will cause many of his listeners to take more interest in this fascinating subject, and to thank the Authorities for having chosen as one of this series of lectures "Man's attempts to gain the empire of the air." An object well worthy of the name of this Institute, "Imperial."

The appeal for financial support is noteworthy. A previous biographer has indicated that Pilcher possessed modest private means, but the evidence suggests that lack of money was a continual problem. In a letter to aeronautical historian J. E. Hodgson dated April 8, 1925, Pilcher's sister Ella wrote, "My brother would have been able to go ahead much faster with less risk had it not been for want of funds. But in those days even one's best friends laughed at attempts at flying & we had to cut our expenditure very fine."[52]

One of the "other things" that had distracted Percy from his gliders had arisen in the latter part of the year. While dining at Stanford Hall, near Rugby, Warwickshire, as the guest of Lord Braye, whose son, the Honorable Adrian Verney Cave, was an old friend from his naval days, Percy was introduced to an Irishman, Walter Gordon Wilson. Born at Dunardagh, Black Rock, County Dublin, on April 22, 1874, Wilson, like Pilcher, had served in the Royal Navy as a midshipman and at the time of their meeting had just come down from Cambridge.[53]

Verney Cave, Wilson, and Pilcher, who was seven years older than the other two, shared a lively interest in the "exciting new mechanical developments of the time." All three were "exceedingly good draughtsmen," and Verney Cave was "quite a talented artist." The trio were also "practical in engineering matters and extremely ingenious." In fact, both Wilson and Verney Cave had wired their respective fathers' homes for electric light.

Pilcher and Wilson "shared a love of sailing small boats,"[54] and during the dinner they discussed "some sailing race[s] and boat sailing in general."[55] Percy, who was reputed to have already made a boat with a windmill-driven propeller, remarked that it was possible to construct a sail that did not cause the boat to heel over in the wind. The same idea had occurred to Wilson, and they soon agreed to put the theory into practice together.

The Wilson family possessed a variety of small boats, which they sailed in Queenstown Harbour (now Dun Laoghaire), close to Dunardagh. The previous year Walter had bought a 17-foot boat from another friend, Prof. "Joe" Barcroft, and he agreed to convert this craft for the experiments, the initial work being carried out at Dunardagh to their joint designs.[56]

Surviving records of these experiments are fragmentary, but the work certainly continued well into 1897. From the evidence of surviving photographs it seems that the first "Cyclone sail" to be built was circular, and resembled an umbrella in the way it was furled around the mast and opened up. Pictures dated September 10, 1896,[57] show that the sail owed much to Pilcher's wing structures in its method of construction, having sixteen radial ribs contained in sleeves stitched to the undersurface of the sail, and generous wire bracing to stay it in position.

The mast to which this strange sail was attached was equally unconventional. Its base was fixed to a universal joint and it could be raised and lowered and fixed at any inclination, pointing forward or to either side of the boat, being attached via tackle and pulleys to a central pivot or "Samson post." Weights or springs were provided to counterbalance the weight of the mast and sail.

Not only did this arrangement eliminate the boat's tendency to heel over, but the sail actually lifted the boat in the water, thereby reducing the drag of the hull as it was driven forward.

The first "Cyclone sail," being tested by Wilson and Pilcher. Dated September 10, 1896, this picture was probably taken during early trials in Ireland. Wilson is wearing the dark jacket. (Author)

The "Cyclone sail" was the subject of British Patent No. 29,194, applied for on December 19, 1896, and accepted—in updated form—on December 11 the following year.[58] In the words of the inventors: "In beating or with the wind on the beam this [arrangement] is a distinct advantage because the pull then by the sail is upward from the lee side and not from the side to windward of the keel, whereby the chances of a capsize are practically removed."

The "Cyclone sail" was to undergo development during the next year. Its final form and eventual fate are described in the next chapter.

3

A New Form of Locomotion, 1897

January 1897 saw Pilcher back on the lecture circuit. On the afternoon of Thursday the 21st, he spoke before the Military Society of Ireland in the Royal University Buildings, Dublin, on "Experiments in Flying Machines." How he came to give this lecture is of interest. Captain Baden-Powell, then honorary secretary of the Aeronautical Society of Great Britain (ASGB), was serving with the Scots Guards at Richmond Barracks, Dublin.[1] It is also probable that Percy's elder brother, Thomas, was serving as a staff officer in Dublin at the same time.[2] It takes little imagination to conceive of a "conspiracy" between these two gentlemen to arrange for Percy to give his talk. Maj.-Gen. Lord Frankfort de Montmorency, commanding the district, presided, and there was reported to be "a fairly large attendance."[3]

This was the only lecture given by Pilcher to be printed in pamphlet form,[4] and it is obvious that its first part was simply a shortened version of the opening of his 1895 Glasgow University lecture. He omitted the discussion of the scientific and technical aspects and, after covering Lilienthal's work up to the time of his death, described his own experiments and gliders. It seems to have been the first occasion on which the name of his latest glider was announced. He had decided to call it the "Hawk," and he had the machine hanging overhead in the lecture theater. The talk was illustrated "by a series of well executed lantern slides"[5] and by demonstrations of two model gliders, one with a tailplane and one without. It was reported that "the single surface model, after a series of turns, fell close to the platform, while the double surface sailed smoothly over the heads of the audience and fell at the extreme end of the hall." Pilcher also had a paper cone and a weighted parachute dropped from the roof to compare dihedral stability and the oscillation caused by a low center of gravity. He stood in the Hawk to show the position of the glider when landing—"weight well back, and the machine tipped up in front."[6]

The original notes for this lecture, now in the library of the Royal Aeronautical Society (RAeS) in London, contain the only known direct reference to the study of birds by Percy and Ella. These observations—omitted from the printed lecture—show that these studies had proved to Percy that Lilienthal's emphasis on the need for a horizontal tail was correct:

> During the summer we kept several young birds—we propose to notice their attempts at flying. One in particular—a young diver showed very clearly the absolute necessity of a horizontal rudder. This bird had scarcely any tail—& it kept pitching over on to its beak exactly as I had done before I added the horizontal rudder.
>
> We also had a young sparrow which was very tame, & used to fly about the room all day & sleep in a biscuit tin at night & we noticed that whenever it had injured its tail in its tin at night—as it often did—it absolutely refused to attempt to fly—if one poked it & made it start it would always land on its beak.[7]

One feature of the Lilienthal gliders that Pilcher pointed out to his audience was the addition of two pads positioned on short struts behind the pilot "with which his shoulders come in contact, when his arms were almost straight, to prevent him from tumbling through and breaking his arms." Pilcher added that Lilienthal had broken his wrist before these were fitted, when, "having thrown his weight very far back he was unable to pull himself up again." Strangely, Pilcher had not fitted similar pads to the Hawk initially, though they were added later.

Describing the pilot's position, he said:

> This method of support, although it appears uncomfortable, is not really so bad as it seems, and one can soon get accustomed to it. It allows one great freedom in moving one's weight about, and gives one an excellent command of the machine when standing on the ground. It has often been suggested that it would be a good plan to have a pair of stirrups to fit one's feet into while in flight, to have a net to sit in, or

some such device to relieve the weight on the arms; but so far the length of the flight has never been so long as to make such a thing necessary, and anything of this kind would be an incumbrance, and would hinder free movement, fidget one, and keep one from slipping out of the machine quickly in case of accident.

Passing reference was made to the fact that a No. 11 Lilienthal glider was owned by Prof. G. F. Fitzgerald of Trinity College, Dublin. Fitzgerald had purchased his glider from Lilienthal in 1895, but had made only half-hearted tests—including flying it as a kite—before abandoning his experiments.[8]

Once again Pilcher referred to his intentions to make a machine similar to the Hawk:

but having an oil engine situated just in front of me on the machine, with a shaft passing over my head, working a screw propeller of about four feet diameter, situated behind me. The machine will be started in exactly the same way as the soaring machines, by running down an incline, and when in the air the screw will be started to revolve, and in this way I hope to be able to maintain horizontal flight. . . . It appears that an expenditure of energy of about two H.P. . . . is necessary, I shall therefore use an engine of about four H.P., because of inefficiency of the screw and other losses. The flying speed would be about 30 miles per hour.

While the means of starting the propeller in midair remains unexplained, the doubling of the engine's power was a promising improvement.

Percy also believed that the application of power would improve the machine's natural stability. His original lecture notes contain the following paragraph, omitted from the printed version:

It should be much easier to keep a true balance in the air when a motive power has been added—for in soaring it is less difficult to balance with a wind than without one, & in watching birds we can see how much less they have to balance themselves when they are flapping their wings than when they are soaring with their wings outspread & still.[9]

The final part of the lecture was devoted to Maxim's experiments, and dwelt mainly on his giant aircraft of 1890–94. Pilcher stated that Maxim had been inspired to embark on the work by seeing, in 1889, "some very thin and good steel tubes which were made in France, and he became convinced that with their use a practical flying machine could be made." Percy commented: "It is interesting to note the peculiar way in which the engineering mind works, from the detail to the whole; from the tubes to the flying machine."

"Since this [the accident of 1894]," concluded Pilcher, "Mr. Maxim has done very little. I am now working with him, and I believe that we are shortly going to begin a new machine of quite a new type, about which I am not at liberty to speak." This is obviously another allusion to the helicopter mentioned in the previous chapter.

The ensuing discussion was led by Baden-Powell, who compared Pilcher's small machines with Maxim's behemoth, and sensibly remarked, "Until we have some experience in knowing how to manage a small machine, we cannot hope to be able to manage a big one." Nor was the military potential of a practical airplane beyond the captain's conception: "If we can only get a machine which will travel about in the air, and be able to go a good many miles through the air at a considerable height up, a great deal could be done, not only in the way of observation of the enemy, but also in the way of attacking fortifications and positions from above."

The most farsighted prophecy came from Major-General Frankfort, who, in concluding the discussion and proposing a vote of thanks to the lecturer, referred to the potential of aerial bombardment, adding, "Two people can play at that game, so that if we had our machine in the air, probably the enemy would have their machine also, and it would probably come to the two machines trying to get at each other." The audience laughed at this prophetic vision of aerial combat.

"A few years ago," he concluded, "if anybody suggested that bicycles should be used in the army, they would be laughed at. . . . However, every army is using the cyclists now, and probably before many years are over we shall have flying machines in the same way."

Exactly a week later, on January 28, Percy read a paper before a fortnightly meeting of the Glasgow University Engineering Society, "having travelled specially from London for that purpose." This seems to have been more concerned with Maxim's work, for it was reported that it "took the form of extracts from an essay by Mr. Maxim prepared two years ago for the Smithsonian Institute [*sic*], Washington." Pilcher again referred to plans to power a glider with Maxim's help. Percy's old boss, Professor Biles, presided, and both he and Professor Barr expressed "admiration of Mr. Pilcher's pluck" and wished him "success and freedom from accident in future."[10]

Shortly after the acceptance of his flying-machine patent on March 6, Percy was elected a member of the ASGB. This took place at a meeting of the council on March 26, when Professor Fitzgerald and Mr. T. J. Bennett, the only owners of Lilienthal gliders in the British Isles, were also recruited. Fitzgerald was also elected to the council at the same meeting.[11]

Production of the printed pamphlet of the Dublin lecture was delayed owing to Pilcher's preoccupations. On Sunday, April 4, he wrote to Baden-Powell from Victoria Street, saying, "I am very busy now and have done nothing about re-writing the lecture so will you just print an abstract of it and I will try & give you an article with new illustrations in a month or two."[12]

This referred to Baden-Powell's wish to publish the Dublin lecture in the ASGB's newly launched quarterly *Aeronautical Journal.* A précis, concentrating on Percy's own work, duly appeared in the April issue, in which his election was also announced.[13]

The letter continued: "I most unfortunately took my machine out on a *very* squally day a week ago & got drifted sideways fast. One wing tip caught & I got turned right upside down—it smashed up the wing pretty badly."[14] A quick sketch depicted this rather nasty mishap, which must have been disheartening right at the start of the new season. Had a fin been fitted, it could have been avoided.

In May 1897 the third issue of the *Aeronautical Annual* appeared. Launched in 1895 and edited by James Means of Boston, Massachusetts, an aeronautical enthusiast and friend of Chanute, the *Annuals* had quickly become essential reading for those interested in the progress toward heavier-than-air flight. They contained articles by many of the leading pioneers, including Lilienthal, Maxim, and Chanute. The 1897 edition, which was to be the last, was the only one to contain a short contribution from Pilcher outlining his work to date (probably late 1896), and stating that a seventeen-second towed flight in the Bat was "the longest time I have ever been off the ground."[15]

Referring to his first tests of the Hawk in 1896, he states: "In this machine I did away with the vertical rudder [fin] altogether. For days when there is not much wind the machine is quite manageable as it is, but for squally days I think that a vertical rudder should be added.

With this machine I have twice cleared nearly 100 yards, once with a slight wind and once in a dead calm." After mentioning the "bush flight" once again, he adds, "I have also been able to steer sideways to a limited extent by moving the weight of my body towards the side to which I wanted the machine to turn." The wheels, he said, "are a great convenience for moving the machine about, and often save the framework from getting broken if one lands clumsily. The wheels are backed by stiff springs which can absorb a considerable blow."

Turning to his plans for a powered glider, Pilcher wrote:

> A new machine is now being built which will have an oil engine to drive a screw-propeller. With this machine without the engine, I drop 50 feet in 10 seconds; that is at the rate of 300 feet per minute; taking my weight and the weight of the machine at 220 pounds the work lost per minute will be about 66,000 foot-pounds or 2-horse power. When I have been flown as a kite (i.e. under tow) it seems that about 30 pounds pull will keep me floating at a speed of about 2,200 feet per minute, or 25 miles an hour. 30 × 2,200 = 66,000 foot-pounds = 2-horse power, which comes to just the same thing.
>
> An engine is now being made which will, I hope, exert enough power to overcome the losses arising from friction and [propeller] slip, and keep the new machine floating horizontally. Of course for the same wing surface the machine will have to sail faster in order to keep afloat with the extra weight of the engine, and more power than the 2-horse power will therefore have to be used.
>
> About 170 square feet seems to be the best area for a machine of this class for a man of average weight; if it is made larger the machine becomes heavier, and is much more difficult to handle because of its increased size and weight, and if it is smaller its sailing speed becomes unpleasantly great.

The last two paragraphs pinpoint the dilemma that Pilcher faced. The extra weight of the engine meant that his glider would have a higher stalling speed unless the wing area was increased; if the wing area was increased, the machine not only became heavier still, but it also became impossible to control by weight-shift alone. Any reduction in wing area meant that the speed became even greater. Whichever way he turned, Percy had to pay a penalty. He elected to keep the wing area at the optimum 170 square feet and to accept a higher flying speed.

The ultimate solution to this problem lay in the use of pilot-operated control surfaces at the extremities of the wings and tail—the now-familiar ailerons, rudder, and elevators—which would enable the pilot to exercise the necessary leverage to control large wing areas. Pilcher was totally dependent upon weight-shift control, however, and the physical limitations thereby imposed on his gliders were persistent obstacles in his path on the road to powered flight.

Pilcher applied for two patents in May 1897, his only two for the year. The first of these, No. 11,331 of May 6, related to "engines," but was abandoned, and its content is unknown. The second, No. 11,619 of May 10, was granted. This concerned "Improvements in and connected with Engines actuated by Mixed Products of Combustion and Steam." The engine described was probably not suitable for use in aircraft of the type that Percy was building, but would have been more suited to industrial applications. However, as will be seen later, he did have plans to build a steam-powered glider.

In simple terms, the engine comprised a water-filled boiler "fired by means of oil [petrol] or gaseous fuel," the air to support combustion being introduced into the central furnace by a compressor. Water circulated around the engine and into a coil inside the furnace, where it was heated to form steam. The steam passed out by a jet into the furnace to induce a current, and the products of the combustion and the steam then passed into the cylinder of the engine, which was provided with a water jacket and inlet and exhaust valves. The engine was also used to operate the compressor, and the cooling water could be circulated and converted to steam in the boiler.

By this "mixed medium" system, Pilcher apparently hoped to obtain high efficiency, but his thinking was probably misguided. It seems that high specific power was required, but that the efficiency would have been rather low. The patent was accepted on April 16, 1898, but no record of the engine's practical application has been traced.

In June 1897 Pilcher gave what was probably the first public demonstration of his skills. "A large party of scientists and others" was invited to Upper Austin Lodge at Eynsford on Sunday the 20th "to witness the trial of a new soaring machine."[16] Percy was evidently hoping to attract the interest and financial support of wealthy sponsors to further his work, and one of the gentlemen invited to Eynsford was none other than Douglas Archibald, with whom he had exchanged views on the problem of stability during the previous year. If Percy hoped to prove his point to Mr. Archibald by means of a practical demonstration, he seems to have succeeded, for Archibald wrote an enthusiastic report of the event for the *Pall Mall Gazette.*[17] The essence of his account reads as follows:

> As the party of visitors alighted from the train at Eynsford, most of us with our cycles as had been recommended, we looked like a local cycle club out for a grind. No one saw the stern resolve and deep-set purpose in our eyes as we set off in Indian file along the flinty lane to the ideal valley where Mr. Pilcher is so pluckily and energetically helping to establish a new and, when safe, most delightful form of locomotion. Here, in the huge shed formerly used by Mr. Maxim for the trial of his monster, we discussed tea, accompanied by a most interesting lecture by Mr. Pilcher on the habits and manners of the machine, illustrated graphically by the inventor himself. And here I hope I may be permitted to remark that Mr. Pilcher has been, fortunately, blessed with the possession of a sister, who not only acted as the presiding goddess of the tea-table on the present occasion, but actually made most of the wing surfaces with her own hands.[18]

After describing the Hawk and mentioning that Percy considered both "double planes" and "automatic arrangements for working a tail" to be dangerous, Archibald continues:

> After tea the soaring machine was duly escorted up to the top of the grassy hill, whence the flight was to be made. Meanwhile, a rope which is now used both to prevent accidents and to supply the place of a motor was stretched from the machine down the valley and up the opposite slope where three men and a pulley enabled it to be hauled in at about twenty miles an hour.
>
> During the delay in fixing the rope a most amusing accident occurred. A young lady, bent on soaring into the empyrean, was placed in the machine, which was then run down hill by Mr. Pilcher with his customary energy. The motion sufficed to raise the machine and its occupant, who sailed gracefully down the hill. All would have gone well had not the fact remained unnoticed that a man with a large camera, for securing a series of photos of Mr. Pilcher when in flight for the animatograph, stood directly in the path. Crash went the soaring machine, lady and all, into the camera, which was hurled violently to the ground. Of course, we all thought it was all over with the animato-

graph, but the operator assured us the films had sustained no damage. Two conclusions instantly occurred to my mind. One was the efficiency of the soaring machine as a substitute for cavalry in warfare, and the other was the remarkable vitality of the animatograph.

And now came the climax of the afternoon.

The party with the other end of the rope, ably marshalled by Miss Pilcher, having signalled that all was right, Mr. Pilcher started the machine directly towards the wind, which was blowing gently up the hill. After a preliminary hop, skip, and a jump, the man and machine rose gracefully into the air from the side of the hill, until a height of fully seventy feet in altitude had been reached, when they described a gradually-descending curve towards the valley. Just then, unfortunately, the rope which was converting the entire affair into a huge man-kite, broke, and the machine was left to its own devices and the mercy of the wind.

Here I think came the real inwardness of the experiment. Instead of turning turtle or behaving in an unseemly manner, the apparatus and its operator, who balanced himself with the skill of a professional acrobat, came down in a gentle and dignified manner fully one hundred and fifty yards from the spot whence he started. An involuntary cheer and clapping of hands told at once that we had all recognised the splendid conquest of the powers of the air exhibited by the behaviour of the machine and its inventor. Had the rope remained intact, the machine would have crossed the valley at the height of 150 ft. above its lowest point. As it was, the longest flight with a soaring machine yet made had probably been accomplished. Replace the rope with a motor and the flying machine was within a measurable distance. I had come prepared, like the prophet of old, to criticise. I departed more than ever convinced that, given a few more enthusiasts like Mr. Pilcher and the application of some of the capital which is at present wasted on hypothetical gold mines, we ought to be able to fly before the dawn of the twentieth century.

Several interesting points are raised by this marvelous contemporary eyewitness account. First, the identity of the courageous "young lady" who essayed a free glide down the hill can now be revealed. Writing on July 1, 1959, a cousin of Percy, Lt. Col. W. S. Pilcher, recalled "a flight in his [Percy's] glider made by my sister, the late Miss D. R. Pilcher at Lord Braye's Residence when she landed on top of the Press cameras, smashing several of them."[19] While this distant

Dorothy Rose Pilcher, a cousin of Percy, was one of the first women to fly in a heavier-than-air aircraft, making a short towed glide in the Hawk on June 20, 1897. This portrait was taken in 1909. Percy's sister Ella also made a towed flight. (Diana Pilcher)

recollection of events that occurred some sixty-two years before is obviously somewhat confused, there can be little doubt that Miss D. R. (Dorothy Rose) Pilcher was the young lady (this has been confirmed by Lieutenant Colonel Pilcher's son, Anthony),[20] and the collision with the "Press" must refer to the unfortunate "animatograph" operator. However, the scene of the event has become confused with the scene of Percy's fatal accident two years later. It is most unlikely that there were two incidents in the late 1890s in which a young lady flying the Hawk collided with a cameraman. We can be quite sure that Lieutenant Colonel Pilcher knew that his sister was the lady in question, nonetheless. This is believed to be the earliest recorded instance of a woman flying in a heavier-than-air aircraft, though it is known that Percy's sister Ella also flew under tow in one of his gliders on an undisclosed date.[21]

Furthermore, we can be quite certain of the identity of the cameraman as well. In its issue of August 12, 1897, *Nature* carried another eyewitness report of the Eynsford demonstration.[22] Its author was William J. S. Lockyer, an astronomer, balloonist, and enthusiastic photographer—and a pioneer of aerial photography—who had belittled Pilcher's work the previous year.[23] Lockyer's account was illustrated by a sequence of seven "stills"—"enlargements of six [*sic*] out of the numerous pictures taken during flight by means of the cinematograph." After describing the Hawk and its means of operation,

Pilcher in the Hawk on top of the "Knob" at Eynsford in 1897. The "slip indicator" string flutters by his left arm. (Smithsonian Institution)

Another view of the Hawk on the "Knob" in 1897. The fin, added during this year, is well shown. Ella stands by the tail. (Lord Braye)

Lockyer provided a similar description of Percy's flight, though not in such elaborate prose as Archibald. Some additional or conflicting details are given. The tow "rope" was a "thin fishing-line, 600 yards long," and the end across the valley "passed through two blocks placed close together on the ground at a distance from the aero-plane of about 550 yards. These blocks were so arranged that a movement of the aerial machine in the horizontal direction corresponded to a fifth of the movement of the [three] boys pulling on the line." Tension on the line was said to be "only about 20 lb."

Pilcher flies the Hawk under tow from the "Knob" in 1897. The thin tow line, just visible on the original print, goes off to the top right-hand corner of the picture from the glider's nose. (Trustees of the Science Museum, London)

A towed flight from the "Knob" in 1897. Pilcher is swinging his legs back to decrease speed. Maxim's hangar is visible in the valley on the extreme right.

Lockyer estimated the distance covered before the line snapped at 180 yards, and stated that "a graceful landing was made at a distance of 250 yards from the starting point." He makes no mention of being swooped upon by a flying female shortly beforehand, but then his account is of a more sober nature than Archibald's. Plans to fit a 4-horsepower engine, "considerably more than sufficient for flights of

Pilcher and Wilson (nearest) test the second version of the "Cyclone sail" at Cowes on the Solent in August 1897. The similarity of the sail to the wings of the Hawk is obvious. (Beken & Sons)

moderate length," are mentioned, as is the need for "considerable private means" or financial support.

Lockyer's estimate of 250 yards is usually quoted—without acknowledgment—by historians, who persistently quote the date of the event as June 19. However, the present author bases the date of June 20 on an item in the *Western Mercury* (Plymouth) for Saturday June 12, 1897, which refers to the demonstration taking place "A week tomorrow."[24] The distance covered must remain vague, as no measurements were taken, but the *Aeronautical Journal* for July set it at "about 150 yards."[25] More unfortunately, no trace has yet been found of Lockyer's film, almost certainly the earliest film of an airplane in flight over Great Britain, and one of the earliest in the world to record a heavier-than-air flight. One thing that the stills reproduced in *Nature* reveal is that by this time a small fixed fin of fabric, stretched inside a pyramid of bamboo struts above the tailplane, had been added. A photograph of the Hawk taken at Eynsford during 1897 shows that Pilcher was again using a string slip-indicator, which can be seen tied to one of the mast bracing wires, close to Percy's left arm.[26]

During the first week of August the ultimate version of the Cyclone-sail boat was "very conspicuous at Cowes on the Solent."[27] While the basic principles and method of construction remained the same as for the 1896 version, the new sail was made oval in shape to increase its area, and it looked even more like a pair of Percy's glider wings. However, this unit could not be folded around the mast like an umbrella, so the ribs were built to fold down, fanlike, along each side of the mast. The sail was rigged to a secondary structure, a light girder attached to the mast so that it could pivot. By this means not only could the mast be tilted relative to the boat, but the sail could be set at various angles to the mast. The *Illustrated London News* put it simply: "Roughly speaking, the pull of the sail is at right angles to its mean surface, that is to say, in the direction of the mast. In other words, it may be described as a kite held by a rigid string. . . . When actually sailing in the boat, the only way in which one is aware of a puff of wind is by noticing that the boat travels faster, and experiencing a slight sensation similar to that coming from the acceleration of the engines of a steamer." The mounting of the mast and sail on a "turntable" with a counterbalance was retained. Two tackles were provided to facilitate the elevation and lowering of the mast. The final sail measured 30 feet in "span" and had a "chord" of 16 feet. Although an ordinary rig of 200 square feet of canvas was said to be "rather too much for the boat," it was claimed to be able to carry 360 square feet with the Cyclone sail, and was therefore much faster.

The same issue of *Nature* in which Percy's Eynsford demonstration was described contained a letter from him describing the Cyclone sail.[28] In part, it stated:

> The wind pressure acts practically at right angles to the mean surface of the sail. When the wind is making a large angle with the sail, the centre of pressure is almost at the centre of the surface, but when the wind strikes the sail at an acute angle, as in all sails or kites, the centre of pressure moves towards the weather edge; but by suitably adjusting the sail, the desirable result of obliterating all heeling movement has been achieved.
>
> In practice this result has been obtained by putting more sail to leeward than to windward of the mast, and also by placing the sail not quite at right angles to the mast, but more raised on the lee side.

Pilcher stated that it took only one minute to set or furl the sail. Its object, he added, was "to be able to sail without inclining the boat, so that the limit of driving force is not governed by the stability of the boat in any way, and also that the boat sailing on an even keel has less resistance than when sailing with a list."

The Cyclone sail appears to have been a qualified success. Wilson recalled, "We had great fun out of this boat, though on the whole I must admit it was a failure. We could not get much to windward, but if we only had a strong soldier's wind we did get some fine turns of speed and were credited with 13 knots, and that out of a 17 ft. boat. However, she was a handful."[29]

Although the *Illustrated London News* reported[30] that Wilson and Pilcher "hoped soon to make arrangements for placing smaller sails of the same type on the market, for use in skiffs, yachts, boats and canoes," and that Messrs. Thornycroft of Chiswick were building a new light boat specially adapted to the sail for Mr. G. Selwyn Edwards of Newbury, who was "interested in its development," nothing further seems to have come of it. The last record of Pilcher's interest in the device was a drawing by him of an "umbrella" sail, dated March 15, 1898. This drawing was in Ella's possession in the 1920s, but its present whereabouts are unknown.[31]

As for the prototype boat and sail, Wilson states that it was sold entire "to a man who thought he could handle her better than we could." "But she proved too much for him," he continues, "and on his first start she went off with such a dash that he was into another boat before he could say anything, and he had to pay for the other wreck as well as his own."[32]

Work on the sail had done much to cement the friendship between Wilson and Pilcher, and they had discovered that they shared common interests in spheres beyond sail design. Wilson was "intrigued by Internal combustion engines and motor-cars," and had purchased a motor tricycle with which to experiment. He had also struck up a friendship with the Honorable C. S. Rolls, who had bought his first car, a Peugeot, the previous year. Wilson later acted as Rolls's mechanic on a number of occasions, including two London-Baldock return runs in one day.[33] His familiarity with internal combustion engines could make a valuable contribution to Pilcher's plans for a powered glider.

Also during August, Percy became involved in somewhat protracted correspondence with Alex McCallum, a Scotsman who was preparing a series of articles entitled "The Navigation of the Air" for the *Glasgow Herald.* McCallum was apparently a parliamentary journalist working in London,[34] and he seems to have visited Percy early in the month, when he borrowed a book of newspaper cuttings.[35] He obviously found the new science of aerodynamics difficult to master, for he wrote to Pilcher from 11 Deauville Road, Clapham Park, London, on August 10, seeking enlightenment on some of the mathematics in the *Aeronautical Annual.* The questions concerned air pressure on flat and curved lifting surfaces, the definition of a tangent to a chord, Chanute's calculations on Lilienthal's tables, a question of angle of attack, and, finally, the "exact definition of the term 'drift.' "[36]

Pilcher divided the letter into eight questions, which he answered in a three-page letter the following day.[37] He pointed out that the reaction of pressure on a plane surface is at right angles to the surface, but is inclined slightly forward on a curved surface. "No curved surface," he added, "will actually drive itself into a horizontal wind—but it will have less resistance for the same lift than a plane surface—When I soar I generally have the forward [leading] edge lower than the after—except when stopping, then I raise it considerably."

On the subject of Chanute's calculations on Lilienthal's tables, Pilcher surprisingly states: "I have not studied these and have lent my book."

After explaining Chanute's reasoning on the angle of attack, Pilcher turned to the term *drift,* pointing out that it "is the *horizontal* resistance to forward motion." "It is also used," he adds, "in the sense of slipping with the wind." Fortunately, this confusing double meaning—which has sometimes tripped up historians—has now been resolved by the adoption of the term *drag* to denote resistance to forward motion.

McCallum was still not sure of himself, for he obviously wrote to Pilcher seeking to pay him another visit at 75 Victoria Street on the afternoon of Monday, August 16. Percy replied on August 13 that he could not promise to be in, and suggested that McCallum "call any time you are passing & try & catch me." He added: "You can come as late as you like after leaving the House—I don't mind you waking me up if I'm asleep."[38]

The meeting probably did not take place, for Pilcher penned a further letter to McCallum on August 18[39] in reply to a letter that does not survive. "So sorry for not being able to answer sooner," says Pilcher, "I thought you understood how to resolve forces." His four-page letter goes on to provide further enlightenment on the way in which the forces acting on a wing resolve themselves. "If this is not clear," he concludes, "I shall be in at 10:30 A.M. tomorrow."

One way or the other McCallum finally grasped the subject, for there are no more letters, and his article was published in four parts in the *Glasgow Herald.* Part three contained diagrams that owed much to Pilcher's patient assistance, and reference to Pilcher's own work appeared in the final part.

Describing the demonstration of June 20, McCallum wrote:

> At the place of the flight there is a very shallow valley between two low hills. The wind was too light for much soaring, and Mr. Pilcher tried a new plan. He laid a small line from the one hill to the other across the valley, and at the windward end rigged up a tackle arrangement, through which the line was so passed that pulling it made the long end travel five times as fast. He fastened this end to his soaring apparatus on the leeward hill top, and gave instructions to three boys at the windward end to run along pulling the line as soon as he rose into the air. They did so, and Mr. Pilcher sailed along practically horizontally for the distance above mentioned [McCallum had quoted "250 yards" as the distance covered]. He had every prospect of continuing his flight as far as the cord reached, which was a distance of 600 yards, but a knot in the line slipped, and he had to descend gently to earth. The pull on the line was estimated at 20 lb. He believes that a motor giving a screw thrust of this amount would keep him going horizontally for an indefinite period, and he is now getting a small oil engine and screw manufactured which will be attached to his soaring machine. The engine will be in front and the screw behind, and to make allowance for loss in transmission and screw efficiency the engine will be of about 4-horse power. The present soaring apparatus weighs 50 lb., but Mr. Pilcher hopes to build one of not more than 30 lb. weight. It is hoped that the engine and propeller will not scale more than from 40 lb. to 50 lb., giving a total maximum weight of 80 lb. The screw will have two wooden blades about four feet from tip to tip, and with this apparatus a speed of 30 miles an hour is hoped for. As the supporting or lifting power of the air is as the speed squared, the extra weight can be carried without increasing the present area of the wings. The experimenter will now be in the position of a bird in so far that he will be able to keep the angle of the wings slightly above the horizontal, and so maintain elevation. The value of the gliding experiments can now be seen, for without them the information as to the effects of

wind pressure, the ability to counteract them, and the best shapes for wings would not have been obtained. The stage has now been reached when a motor may with some profit be tried.[40]

As McCallum obtained much of his information from Pilcher, we can be quite sure that the above is direct reportage of Percy's own words—a valuable outline of his plans for powered flight and the reasoning behind them. His optimistic figures for weight, power, and performance were really unattainable, and the structural soundness of a 30-pound powered glider would have been questionable.

McCallum continues:

> Mr. Pilcher also hopes to experiment with a small steam-engine and propeller fitted to a soaring apparatus, so that he will be able to compare the results got respectively from oil and steam. At first, however, the steam-engine will be made non-condensing, so as to avoid weight and complication, and as the supply of water that can be carried will not be great, the flights must be short. The machine will, however, be useful for short experimental flights. He also intends to make a trial of machines with superposed surfaces as well as with those consisting of a single pair of wings.[41]

Strangely, McCallum was not given a by-line for his articles; the newspaper credited them as "From a correspondent." However, by October 1897 they had been reprinted as a sixpenny (2½ p) pamphlet under the original title, bearing the author's name.[42] Copies were available from Captain Baden-Powell of the ASGB, and the pamphlet was advertised in the Society's *Journal.*

Meanwhile, an event had taken place in the business world that was to have repercussions on Pilcher's experiments. On September 15 the Maxim and Nordenfeld company was taken over by Vickers, to become Vickers, Sons & Maxim Limited.[43] Vickers, which had held a minority shareholding in the company, paid £1,353,000 for the artillery and ammunition works at Erith, Crayford, and Dartford. Owing to a lack of government orders and to "eccentric" management by Maxim and Nordenfeld, the company had not fared well in the 1880s but had been made profitable in 1896 by Sigmund Loewe, whose appointment to the board had been arranged by Lord Rothschild.[44] Loewe's business ability has been described as "one of the most important assets which Vickers acquired" in the purchase,[45] and Vickers was "entirely ruthless" in taking only the people it wanted from companies that it bought. Maxim was "effectively" eliminated from any position of influence.[46]

One consequence of this takeover, and of Maxim's consequent loss of standing in the company, seems to have been that he was required to remove his hangar from the company's ranges at Eynsford. Coupled with Maxim's poor finances following his experiments in the late 1880s and early 1890s, this brought his work to an end. It also deprived Pilcher not only of a hangar, but also of his flying ground.

No records of Pilcher's activities during October 1897 survive, but a significant event took place in the United States on the 20th of the month. This was the delivery of a lecture to the Western Society of Engineers by Octave Chanute. Entitled "Gliding Experiments," it described in some detail the trials of multiplane and biplane gliders made by Chanute and his assistant, the civil and mechanical engineer Augustus Moore Herring, in the desert sand dunes of Indiana, at the southern tip of Lake Michigan during 1896 and 1897.[47] The first experiments, begun in June 1896, started with brief tests of Herring's "copy" of the Lilienthal monoplane. After that, Chanute's multiplane, with a total of twelve planes that could be fitted in various arrangements, was tested. The first tests were concluded on July 4, when the team returned to Chicago.

Here the multiplane was rebuilt as a quadruplane, with an auxiliary surface above the top center section, a single pair of wings acting as a tailplane, and a vertical fin. An "automatic stability system" devised by Chanute, whereby the wings were free to pivot fore and aft against springs to absorb gusts of wind, was modified so that the whole wing cellule on each side pivoted on ball bearings at the wing roots. The cellules were "all trussed together, with vertical posts and diagonal wire tires, this being probably the first application which has been made of the Pratt [bridge] truss to flying machine design," to quote Chanute's own words.[48]

A new and influential glider was also built at this time. Based upon a rubber-powered model biplane designed by Herring in 1893, and originally built as a triplane, it embodied the now traditional structure for multiplanes, with rigid surfaces linked by wooden struts and braced with the Pratt truss. A cruciform tail was fitted, and the pilot hung beneath the lower wing, with his armpits over a pair of "parallel bars." The tail was attached by rods to the bar supports and

Octave Chanute (1832–1910). (Smithsonian Institution)

Chanute's quadruplane glider, tested in the sand dunes by Lake Michigan, Indiana, in 1896, had a significant influence on Pilcher's thinking. (Smithsonian Institution)

was braced with wires incorporating springs. This feature of the design allowed the tail to give in wind gusts, thereby correcting any tendency to veer off course.

Tests were resumed in August 1896 and the performance of the multiplane was much improved. However, the new machine, now modified to biplane format, outshone all that had preceded it, covering distances up to 359 feet. Herring was anxious to fit an engine to the biplane, but Chanute thought it premature to do so.[49] The two experimenters parted, but not before they had applied for two patents, one for the multiplane and, more significantly, one for a powered triplane. (They will be covered in greater detail in chapter 4.) These experiments were to have an important influence on Pilcher's work.

Having parted from Maxim, Pilcher now teamed up with Walter Wilson. According to Wilson, it had been arranged that he "should

The Chanute-Herring biplane, tested shortly after the quadruplane, represented a great advance in glider design and proved safe and easy to master. (Smithsonian Institution)

work with Pilcher and Maxim, but Maxim's funds running low, he stopped his experiments."[50] There is no mention here of the major changes wrought by the Vickers takeover. A new company, Wilson and Pilcher Limited, was registered on November 9, 1897, with Walter Wilson and Percy Pilcher as joint managing directors.[51]

In the company's memorandum and articles of association its work is described, in part, as follows:

> To design, build, construct, repair, convert, alter, sell, let or hire, and otherwise deal in engines of every description, and for every purpose, carriages and vehicles of all kinds, ships, barges, launches, boats and vessels of every description, mills, lifts, dredges and pumps, sails, ship tackle, flying machines, and machinery and apparatus of every kind which can or may be worked or propelled by, or in the working and propulsion of which can or may be utilized, steam power, electricity, gas, wind, or water, or any other motive power, or any combination of different motive powers.
>
> To carry on the business of experimental and consulting engineers, draughtsmen of all kinds of machinery, iron-founders, mechanical, electrical and water supply, engineers and manufacturers of machinery, tool makers, brass founders, metal workers, boiler makers, millwrights, machinists, iron and steel converters, smiths, wood workers, builders, painters, metallurgists, gas makers, carriers, and to design, buy, sell, manufacture, repair, convert, alter, let or hire, and deal in machinery, implements, rolling stock and hardware of all kinds, and to carry on any other business (manufacturing or otherwise) which may seem to the Company capable of being carried on conveniently in connection with the above or otherwise, calculated directly or indirectly to enhance the value of any of the Company's property and rights for the time being.

The capital of Wilson and Pilcher Limited was £10,000, divided into 10,000 shares of £1 each. On October 23 seven persons, including Walter Wilson and Percy Pilcher, had taken 100 shares apiece. The other shareholders were George Orr Wilson Esquire (Wilson's father); H. L. Wilson, lieutenant, Royal Horse Artillery (Wilson's brother); John Frederick Marshall of Brighton, graduate student, Cambridge; James Charles Calder, distiller;[52] and Arthur Trevor Dawson, late lieutenant, Royal Navy.

The number of directors was limited to "not less than two or more than five," and the first directors were Walter Wilson, Percy

Pilcher, and George Orr Wilson, who were to remain in office until the ordinary general meeting in 1899. As managing directors, Walter and Percy were each to be paid £4 per week, plus "one-third each of the net profits of the business in each year, as shown by the annual balance-sheet, after payment of the preference dividend of £3 per centum per annum."

On November 10, 1897, Pilcher wrote to Baden-Powell, enclosing ten shillings and sixpence for a set of ASGB reports for 1866–93.[53] There were twenty-one volumes and they were advertised at one shilling each, or half price to members.[54] Percy also enclosed another sixpence, asking that a copy of McCallum's reprint be sent to Dr. Francis Elgar of 18 York Terrace, Regents Park. Dr. Elgar, a leading naval architect, had been professor of naval architecture and marine engineering in Glasgow University from 1883 to 1886, and from 1892 to 1906 was director of naval architecture to the Fairfield Shipbuilding and Engineering Co. of Glasgow.[55] Almost certainly he had come to know Pilcher during the latter's time at the university and at Elder's, and he was evidently interested in his experiments. Pilcher obviously saw fit to foster Elgar's enthusiasm in the hope of obtaining financial assistance. In a note at the top of the letter, Percy added that he was giving a lecture to the Sesame Club in Dover Street on Monday, November 15, at 8:45 P.M. "Would you care to come?" he asked Baden-Powell, adding, "There will be nothing which is new to you."

Percy's standing in the ASGB took another leap at a council meeting on November 12, when, in his absence, he was elected to the council.[56] Two days later, on Sunday, November 14, he again wrote to Baden-Powell. A general annual meeting of the society was scheduled for Thursday, December 16, in the hall of the Society of Arts, Adelphi. Various members were to speak about their experiments and display their apparatus. Baden-Powell had asked Pilcher to participate, and Percy wrote: "I will try & exhibit my new oil engine at the General Meeting—& some new photos. We have taken a workshop—& will be in order for doing small work by the end of this week—I think we should be very glad to do the fan."[57]

The petrol engine was obviously taking shape, but how far its construction had progressed is unknown. The "fan" was clearly some device developed by Baden-Powell. Unfortunately, we do not have his letter to enlighten us as to its purpose.

On November 21, after the aforementioned Sesame Club lecture on November 15, Pilcher acknowledged a letter and photographs sent by Baden-Powell. He had been notified of his election to the council, and he stated: "I shall be much honoured to be part of the Council of the Society." He was still unsure of the date of the annual meeting, but said, "I have some good photos which I will exhibit & which will do nearly as much as my machine."[58] This suggests that the Hawk was not to be displayed, but, as will be seen later, it was shown at the Adelphi.

The following day, November 22, a notice of situation of Wilson and Pilcher Limited's registered office was filed. The address was 17 Mount Pleasant, Grays Inn Road, London WC.[59]

At the end of the first week of December Pilcher received a letter from the United States. Dated November 29, it was from Octave Chanute,[60] who wrote:

> My Dear Sir,
>
> I have been hoping to see in the prints some accounts of your aeronautical experiments this season, but have thus far seen nothing later than the account in "Nature," of August 12, 1897. I hope that you have continued your work, and have had abundant success, both in gliding and with a motor.
>
> I am still disinclined to apply the latter, as I wish to work out thoroughly the question of automatic stability in the wind, before taking any chances of accident with an engine. I propose to experiment with still a third method of maintaining equilibrium, to make sure as to which is absolutely safest.
>
> Mr. Herring and I resumed our experiments with our former machine last September. I have sent a brief account of them, with some photographs, to Capt. B. Baden-Powell, which I presume that he will publish, but I enclose herewith some photos which I did not send him, illustrating some other flights. These now number well up to 1,000 without the slightest accident, and I begin to think that we have pretty well eliminated all the hidden defects. Still the man has to move occasionally to preserve his balance on this machine, and my idea is that he should not move at all, except to steer. That the wind itself should readjust the apparatus as often as the equilibrium is compromized, so as to leave the man free to run the motor, and to direct the course.
>
> I shall be very glad to hear from you and to exchange views. I believe success will come only through a process of evolution, and that

the present investigators can only hope to be remembered as having pointed out the way.

Yours Truly
O. Chanute
413 E. Huron St
Chicago, Ill.

Chanute's idea that the glider should be self-stabilizing to leave the pilot free to "direct the course" was a step ahead of Pilcher. But Chanute was never to satisfy himself that the former had been achieved and therefore never devoted much attention to the important matter of control. We do not know which photographs he enclosed, but they were certainly of the successful biplane. As will be seen later, a "pamphlet" was also enclosed—probably a reprint from the *Journal of the Western Society of Engineers* of his paper "Gliding Experiments."

On December 8 Pilcher wrote to Baden-Powell from the workshop of Wilson and Pilcher Limited.[61] His prime purpose in writing was to request more tickets for the ASGB's general meeting on the 16th. "I could I expect send them to about a dozen people who would be worth having—I mean worth having from the Society's point of view." In a footnote he added: "Chanute has sent me some new photos—which I will bring—When shall I get my photos put up?" (at the Adelphi). Hastily written diagonally across the top left-hand corner of the letter is: "We are all ready for taking in work."

The most amazing thing is the speed with which Chanute's letter had reached Pilcher; it was written on November 29 and was in Percy's hands by December 8. Quite a tribute to the postal system of 1897.

Pilcher continued to campaign for members on the society's behalf. He wrote to Baden-Powell again on December 12 from 15 Kensington Court Palace, requesting "membership forms & Journal subscription forms" and asking whether an invitation to the forthcoming meeting had been sent to Mr. Yarrow.[62] This refers to A. F. Yarrow, later Sir Alfred Yarrow, the prominent Glaswegian shipbuilder, whom Pilcher obviously had in mind as another potential patron.

The general annual meeting of the ASGB at the Society of Arts on December 16 was fully reported in the January 1898 issue of the *Aeronautical Journal.* Short talks were given by Major Moore on the subject of flying models imitating the action of the flying fox; by Mr. E. S. Bruce on an electrically operated signaling balloon; by Mr. Spiers on the life-saving kites developed by himself and his father; by Captain Baden-Powell on man-lifting kites and a rather crude pair of "bird-like" wings that he attached to himself with the idea of running down a hill and giving "a jump and a couple of flaps," "to get the idea of the effect of flapping wings as a propeller"; and, of course, by Pilcher on his "soaring machine."

Various exhibits were ranged around the hall. Baden-Powell's wings stood against a wall at the back, Major Moore's "neat-looking" silk model flying fox was to the right of the platform, Mr. Bruce's signaling balloon shared a corner with Captain Spier's life-saving kite, Baden-Powell's "large kite" was on one side of the room, and to the left of the platform was the "Aeroscope," a device that showed "the course of currents of air impinging on plane and curved surfaces." Also on show were a "large artificial feather" and "many photographs." Suspended over the center of the hall and dominating the proceedings was "Mr. Pilcher's great soaring machine"—the Hawk.

Pilcher opened his address by drawing attention to his glider and describing it as "the one I have done best in." "The other day," he remarked, "I cleared nearly 300 yards in it. Now the object of these soaring machines, or rather the use of them, is to learn how to manage the simplest and cheapest machine in the air that can possibly be made. They are flying machines without any engines." Furthermore, he added, breakages did not "really matter much."

Percy then described his method of flying under tow, saying: "This machine takes a pull of between 20 and 30 lbs. to keep it in horizontal flight with me in it; and I weigh about 140 lbs., the machine is about 50 lbs., that is 200 lbs. To keep that in horizontal flight with 20 lbs. pull, means a pull of only about one-tenth of the weight of the machine."

The significant points here are that Pilcher regarded his gliders strictly as steps toward powered flight—not as gliders for gliding's sake, and that his aim was to achieve horizontal flight—not to soar on upcurrents, as some historians of gliding have stated. In fact, there is not one iota of contemporary evidence to support this claim.

Outlining his technique for holding the glider and describing the position to be adopted, he remarked: "The great difference between a human being and a bird is that we are most misshapen things for the purpose of flying; we expose an enormous frontage to the wind, whereas a bird is nicely shaped away; although I am rather proud of these machines, they are not nearly as smooth and nicely finished off as birds are."

Questions were directed at the speaker by Thomas Moy, an engineer who, with Richard Shill, had tested an unpiloted "aerial steamer" on a circular track at the Crystal Palace during 1873–74. One of Moy's questions was: "Have you tried the super-posed plane?" As will be seen, he had a specific reason for asking this.

Pilcher replied: "I have a machine with super-posed surfaces in hand," but added, "I think I can do just about as well with a single-surface machine as has been done with the super-posed surface machines." He went on to express, once again, his suspicion that the "parachute action" of them would be "very much less" in the event of stalling.

Referring to his tailplane, with its acute negative angle, he remarked:

> Without the rudder you cannot handle the machine at all; it is much too slippery, it will go down in front, and then it will rear up, but the horizontal rudder being slightly raised makes the thing very much steadier, it keeps the machine from pitching suddenly. The thing to be afraid of is taking a header. You are not really so likely to go back the other way, though it is possible.

"The little vertical rudder [fin]," he continued, "has a little bit of a weather-cock action. If the wind suddenly shifts, it swings the machine round to head the wind."

On the subject of "steering," Percy said:

> If you want to turn in the air you get on to that side of the machine towards which you want to turn; that is to say the machine will always turn towards the lower wing. If the wind shifts, and you get a puff from one side, get right over to that side so that the machine will turn that way and tend to head it. Once you are off in the air, it is the relative wind you feel; I mean the wind made in relation to you, not the real wind.

Pilcher spoke of Lilienthal's inspiration, adding a wry touch of humor with the remark: "Unfortunately about a year ago he came to grief, and so I have been trying to do justice to him as a pupil—[laughter]—not in coming to grief, I hope."

Describing the manner in which the Hawk could be folded up, he stated that it could fit into a "comparatively small crate."

Once more he turned to the matter of applying power:

> Now that I have learned to handle one of these things more or less, I have got an oil engine in hand of about 4 h.p., which I think should be enough to keep me in horizontal flight. The pull on a line attached to the machine is between 20 and 30 lbs., the speed at which the machine floats is about 20 or 25 miles an hour. If you multiply that out you come to about 2 or 3 h.p. Consequently, I have been intending simply to put a screw propeller, driven by an oil engine, into the machine, and I hope in time what are now soaring machines will develop into bona fide flying machines.

After describing the installation he added:

> I am not quite sure whether I shall put the engine in this machine or in another; but not a larger machine. I cannot handle a larger machine; it gets too cumbersome. If we put a greater weight into the machine of a certain size, it only means that to float it you will have to sail faster; a limit has to come in somewhere. I have tried various machines, from 150 lbs. to 300 lbs.; but I find about 170 seems to be about as much as one can handle—otherwise a little bit of irregularity in the wind throws one all over the place.

(The figures should refer to wing areas—150, 300, and 170 square feet, but the error passed into print unnoticed.)

"You will have an additional weight in the machine, therefore," interjected Moy.

"The propeller does not weigh much—3½ lbs.," Pilcher responded, "and the oil engine will weigh about 40."

Moy remarked: "I understand that Mr. Chanute is doing the same thing in America." (As will be seen, he knew a great deal about this.)

Pilcher replied that he was aware of Chanute's work and of his reluctance to fit an engine yet. "They have had an oil engine," he said, "but they have had a little trouble in trying to get it to ignite."

He continues:

> The screw is 5 feet in diameter, the pitch is about 4 feet, and about 3 ft. 6 in. in the centre. It is made of yellow pine, and covered with canvas, and is exceedingly stiff and strong. This machine, with the screw propeller and engine, would become a Maxim type of machine, the smallest possible kind to carry a man. I look upon it as a mistake to make anything bigger than one can possibly help, because the weight and expense, and the danger, and everything else seems to me to increase with the increase in size.

By this time even Maxim himself, champion of the large flying machine, had come to this conclusion. In a letter to the *Times* for June 16 the previous year he had written: "If machines are to be made on the aeroplane system small ones will be found to work much better than large ones."[63]

The interrelated problems of stability, control, size, and weight were the subject of a statement by Prof. G. H. Bryan, FRS,[64] who wrote:

> If any experimenter can so thoroughly master the control of a machine sailing down-hill under gravity as to increase the size of the machine and make it large enough to carry a light motor, and if, further, this motor can be made of sufficient horse-power, combined with lightness, to convert a downward into a horizontal or upward motion, the problem of flight will be solved. The first flights need not be long—a hundred yards, rising, say, twenty or thirty feet above the ground, will be sufficient; all else will be simply a matter of improving on the original model. . . . Another promising direction for success lies in an elaborate and exhaustive [mathematical] investigation of balance and stability, such as would allow the safe use of motor-driven machines too large to be controlled by mere athletic agility.

Not only does Bryan's perceptive statement put the mastering of control before the application of power, but it reveals his realization of the need to develop a means of "balancing" an airplane by means other than body-swinging. Regrettably, no practical experimenters were to make thorough tests of such control systems until the turn of the century. Beside the need for an adequately powerful yet light motor, this was the stumbling block of the early pioneers, for, as Bryan pointed out, the need to control a machine by "athletic agility" alone necessarily restricted its size and weight. He quotes Pilcher as saying: "For an eleven stone man, . . . no soaring machine should weigh more than sixty pounds, because it fags one out too soon, and the strain brought on is too severe."[65]

Finally, it was probably during 1897 that Pilcher acquired an example of Lilienthal's No. 11 "standard" glider. This was given to him by T. J. Bennett of Oxford, now assistant secretary of the ASGB, who had exhibited it at the Imperial Institute the previous year, but passed it on to Pilcher owing to his own "bad health."[66] No record has been traced to suggest that Pilcher or Bennett ever flew this machine, which is now in the care of the Science Museum in London.

4

Transatlantic Influence, 1898

The January 1898 issue of the *Aeronautical Journal,* which contained the report of the ASGB's general meeting of December 16, also contained illustrations of Chanute's biplane glider and the "brief account" that he had mentioned to Pilcher in his letter of November 29, 1897.[1] This article, and Chanute's paper "Gliding Experiments," must have made inspiring reading for Pilcher. By all accounts the biplane flew as well as Lilienthal's monoplane, yet was easier to handle. "Such confidence was acquired in two of the machines [the quadruplane and the biplane]," wrote Chanute, "that all amateurs were welcome to try them under proper supervision, and it was evident that any young, active man could become a gliding expert in a week." "The sport is so fascinating," he added, "that experts can hardly get enough of it."[2] The reports of hundreds of accident-free glides did much to allay Percy's fear of machines with their wings high above the pilot.

Pilcher's enthusiasm is evident in the letter that he penned to Chanute on January 23 from Mount Pleasant, London:[3]

> It was a great pleasure to receive your letter of November 29th, and to know that you are interested in my experiments—I am sorry to say I have not been able to go on with my experiments nearly as fast as I should like—I have done hardly anything since the trials were made & which were published in *Nature* last August—
>
> Thank you very much for your photographs & for the pamphlet they were very interesting—I envy you your beautiful Experimental Ground—I have always had to practice in the most squally places & have seldom been able to choose my day—but in order to be able to

make any trials at all have had to go ahead when opportunity offered itself—

I am very much interested in your work with regard to automatic stability—all that I have tried to do is to make the machine neutral & easy to handle—Without having heard of what you have done, I should have been very sceptical about your high machines, I mean stable machines with the supporting surfaces so far above the man—I cannot help attributing the easiness of handling of my last wings to the surface being so very low down, and so that when a puff of wind strikes me when I am standing there is no tendency, or rather exceedingly little, to knock me over backwards—I have been fortunate in getting the wings also very neutral sideways, I mean to say that if I stand sideways to the wind there is very little tendency for the machine to capsize—I am quite sure that with any of Herr Lilienthals [*sic*] two surface machines I should not have been able to do any good at all, in the places where I have had to carry out my trials—

I intend to make a machine something like one of your multiple sail ones, but without any automatic arrangements—I am anxious to see how I get on with it—

From the tone you have taken all through, I imagine you to be much more desirous of having the general problem of flight solved, than that you should have all the honour—so if you like to send me sketches of one of your latest type machines I will make one, & let you know how I get on with it—

I have, as you will see by this [letterhead] . . . started business independently—we are engineers laying matters out particularly for doing Experimental work—I hope now to have much better opportunity for going on with these most interesting experiments—

I have an oil engine in hand, but which is not yet quite finished, which I hope to put into a machine in the Summer—My experiments are costing a good deal & so I have asked a few people if they would care to form a syndicate, by which they would profit in the event of money being made—Dr. Francis Elgar Mr. A. F. Yarrow Prof. Biles & a few other men interested in scientific subjects have volunteered to join, I should be much obliged if you could give me the names of any gentlemen you think could afford & would be likely to join—

With my best thanks for your letter & paper,

Yours very truly,
Percy S. Pilcher

I am sending a couple of photos.

Pilcher was at last convinced that a safe multiplane could be built and flown. This was the start of a radical change in his design thinking, in which he would turn from deep-chord monoplane wings to narrow-chord multiplane surfaces. His success in persuading some of his shipbuilding contacts from Glasgow to invest in flying machines at a time when such devices were viewed with the utmost skepticism speaks highly of the respect that they must have had for the young Percy's abilities. The engine that was "not quite finished" was, in fact, still quite a long way off. But instead of having good intentions, as reported for the last year or more, Pilcher, aided by Wilson, was at least building one.

Chanute replied from San Diego on February 10:[4]

> I am in Southern California on account of my wife's health, and your pleasant letter Jany 23d has been forwarded to me.
>
> I am greatly pleased with the impression which you have derived from my writings. You are quite right: I am much more desirous of having the general problem of flight solved, than that I shall have all the honour; and for a long time, I fancy, there will be nothing but honour to be expected.
>
> You are very welcome to make and use one of my multiple wing machines, and I hope that you will hit upon improvements to it which shall be all your own. The full plans are in the *Aeronautical Annual* of 1897, but you will find further plans and explanations in a British Patent which will probably issue to me about the time that you receive this letter, being Application No. 13,372 of May 31, 1897. This patent I have applied for, 1st to establish priority, and 2d to prevent premature exhibition and accidents of wandering acrobats, for as you seem to have well discovered, one has to select the best conditions for success, in the present stage of development, and this cannot be done if exhibitions have to be given at set times.
>
> I believe the plans on the patent are full enough to give you what you want, but if not, I shall be glad to send you such explanations as you may desire. The only thing which now occurs to me as likely to bother you is the fore and aft movements of the wings. This has to be done tentatively; setting the springs at a certain tension, making a short glide, and setting them again. Sometimes 8 or 10 tentative glides are required before you feel that the springs are properly adjusted, so as to reduce your own movements to a minimum. I used "8 inch rubber bands" for these springs, doubling them where I thought it was required, and got an action nearly, but not quite automatic.

I regret that I cannot extend to you the same licence to reproduce a "two-surface" machine. This has a regulator designed by Mr. Herring, who believes that money is to be made out of it, and who has left me to work on his own account. He has all my good wishes, but I fear he is working towards an accident.

I presume I shall find your photos on my return to Chicago, in March. Thanks.

Yours Truly,
O. Chanute.

This letter explains why Pilcher was to build a multiplane, rather than copy the far more successful biplane. Chanute's unselfishness and eagerness to help a fellow experimenter are typical of the man. He corresponded with pioneers all over the world, acting as a central "clearinghouse" for the growing body of knowledge on the new science.

A summary of capital and shares for Wilson and Pilcher Limited, made up to March 22, reveals that, although the nominal capital was still £10,000, the total number of shares taken up had risen from 700 to 5,000. However, this did not herald a sudden increase in the number of shareholders; it was simply that George Orr Wilson had increased his holding from 100 shares to 4,400.[5]

On March 23 Pilcher sent a note to Baden-Powell, enclosing some handbills about a forthcoming "lantern lecture" and asking Baden-Powell if he would send them to members of the ASGB. Entitled "Experiments with Flying and Soaring Machines," the lecture was given by Pilcher at the Bishopsgate Institute, London, on Friday, March 25, starting at 7:00 P.M. Admission was free—unless seats were booked in advance.[6]

On April 2 Chanute's British Patent, No. 13,372 for "Improvements in and relating to Flying Machines," was accepted.[7] It had been applied for on May 31, 1897, and related principally to the automatic preservation of equilibrium by allowing the wing cellules on each side of the body to swing back against elastic restraints to ensure that the machine's center of gravity coincided with the center of pressure. As Chanute had written, a clear three-view drawing of his multiplane had been published in the 1897 *Aeronautical Annual,* but two notable additions were made to the design in his patent. A sling seat was provided, and foot-operated levers were linked to the wings to enable the pilot to operate the wing-swinging system deliberately, as a means of control, rather than simply allowing it to operate passively as a means of automatic stability. A cord with a spring "interposed" ran back from the lever, around a pulley on the frame, and forward to a point on the wing bay. Another cord, also incorporating a spring, ran forward to the frame to act as a return device. "By shoving on both pedals," the patent states, "the wings will be pulled back, and the machine will tilt over slightly to the front and glide at a flatter angle. On letting both the levers swing back, the springs pull the wings forward, increasing the angle of incidence, tilting the machine up in front, and slowing its headway. This latter effect will be produced automatically in case the operator accidentally loses his hold on the pedals. By operating one pedal alone, the machine may be steered to the right or left."

Chanute also proposed the use of a rudder operated by "tiller ropes," but added: "It is found, however, in practice, that the rudder is more useful as a vertical tail or keel, since the steering can be most easily accomplished by shoving forward the set of multiple wings on the side opposite to that to which it is desired to go." This last suggestion is a little unfortunate, as it meant that the system did not respond to instinctive reactions. If Chanute had thought to cross the control lines, the turn would have been achieved by pushing forward on the appropriate lever.

Although the pedal-steering device had been tested tentatively by suspending the glider, with a man aboard, into wind between two trees, and although the proposal appears perfectly sound, it was not tried out in free flight because Chanute was not entirely happy with the working of the "automatic regulation."[8]

By June Chanute was back in Chicago, and he wrote to Pilcher again on June 3:[9]

> I wrote to you from California Feb 10th, in answer to your letter of Jan 23d, and I hope that you have made some experiments with the "multiple wing" machine.
>
> Mr. Herring has nearly completed a new "two-surfaced" machine, to which he has applied screw propellers, driven by a compressed air engine. It will probably be tested within a month.
>
> I shall be very glad to learn of your own progress this summer, and to keep you advised as to what we do here.

> I have not received the two photos which you wrote you were about to send me.

Herring had been working on his powered aeroplane since 1897. Originally he had proposed a triplane, but he finally settled for a biplane of 18-foot span, fitted with a cruciform tail incorporating the automatic stabilizing device introduced on the 1896–97 gliders. A light two-wheeled undercarriage was fitted to keep the apparatus off the ground, and, as in the gliders, the operator hung on a frame beneath the lower wing. The small engine (3–5 horsepower) was mounted just above the center section of the lower wing and drove two 5-foot-diameter propellers, a tractor, and a pusher in tandem. The completed machine weighed only 88 pounds. The pilot was to face into wind, lift the machine, start the engine, and take a few steps forward for takeoff. Once airborne, he could draw up his feet and sit on a small platform. Although the aircraft was ready for trial by July 1898, however, various minor setbacks were to force the postponement of tests until October.[10]

Percy dictated a brief note to Chanute on June 24, and it was written in longhand by the Wilson and Pilcher company's secretary:

> Thank you very much for your last letter. We are at present engaged in building an engine, and I hope to make some trials in the autumn.
>
> The photographs were sent as promised, and must, I fear [have] gone astray. I have some more on order, and will be glad to send you copies when they are ready.[11]

On the afternoon of the day he sent the above letter to Chanute, Pilcher attended a lecture before the members of the ASGB in the Hall of the Society of Arts.[12] The speaker was Mr. G. L. O. Davidson, and his subject was "The Flying Machine of the Future." Davidson, like Maxim, had a penchant for aircraft on the grand scale. In fact, he had designed and patented an intercontinental vertical-takeoff airliner. By 1898 Davidson had spent sixteen years studying bird flight: "It is an absolute waste of money," he said, "to experiment with machines of any sort designed for aerial purposes by persons who have not studied or been instructed in the conditions of natural flight, and who cannot truthfully say, 'We know how birds fly.' " Unfortunately, although Davidson firmly believed that he knew how birds flew, he had got it completely wrong. He believed that "the entire energy of flying creatures is employed in obtaining a vertical lift, gravitation being the sole force for forward movement, the angle of inclination being governed at will by means of the tail."[13] In other words, birds progressed by flapping to gain altitude and then gliding for a distance before flapping once again. Because of this belief, Davidson said that "I am quite convinced that no more practical results will be attained by these aerodromes driven through the air by propellers than is now attained by balloons."[14]

In 1897 and 1898 Davidson had been granted two patents for his "Air-Car." The first of these, No. 12,469 of 1896, accepted on June 5, 1897,[15] reveals that the thick-section wing of his aircraft housed no fewer than twenty-two vertical fans, or "lifters," driven by a pulley system from engines in the fuselage. One-way flaps on the wing surface allowed air to pass through the wings in vertical flight but closed to provide a supporting surface for gliding. Extensive tests of "lifters" had been made, for which several sponsors had provided funds. The Air-Car was to span 100 feet, weigh "upwards of 7½ tons," and carry twenty passengers in addition to the engines and crew in its enclosed double-deck fuselage.[16]

Although Davidson was never to produce a practical aircraft, he persisted in his efforts—with the help of several syndicates—until as late as 1912, by which time the design had undergone some basic changes.[17] One thing he did foresee with quite remarkable vision in 1898 was transcontinental air travel:

> There will probably be . . . depots within convenient distance of London and other centres, from whence ocean-going and long-distance cars will start and . . . when you wish to travel to the North, you will press an electric button and a motor car will shortly attend to take you, say, to the Great Northern Depot, after looking in the A.B.C. Airway Guide for information as to the time of starting to suit your convenience.[18]

However, Davidson's casual dismissal of propeller-driven machines must have annoyed Percy, and the lecturer then added insult to injury by remarking: "One gentleman I know is now designing a machine by which he hopes, by pushing with a propeller from behind, to glide up the incline against gravity instead of down the incline with gravity, but I think he will find it difficult."

Pilcher was quick to comment in the ensuing discussion. The *Aeronautical Journal* reports:

Mr. Pilcher questioned the desirability of using the word "lifter" for an appliance already well known as a "propeller" or "screw" mounted vertically. He considered it most desirable to make a careful study of all statistics relating to aerodynamics. For instance, the pressure of the wind on various surfaces had received but little attention from experimenters, and very much was to be learnt from any observations in this line. Anyone who had noted any points likely to be of interest should send the results of their observations to the Hon. Secretary of this Society. Mr. Pilcher also doubted the advantage of constructing a very large apparatus. Thus a little paper model could easily be made to fly, but as the size is increased, difficulties of construction also increase, for as the linear dimensions grow, the thickness also requires to be greater and consequently the weight, so that as the machine becomes larger its weight increases in a greater proportion. Then it also becomes a matter of great difficulty to automatically balance any large machine, and this is a point of great importance. What is known as a "soaring machine," to carry one man, has been constructed with the special object of practising this balancing, especially in landing, and such a machine with suitable engines and propellers, would seem to be the best form of flying machine. To make a large flying-machine without previous experience presents great difficulties. Who could design and practically construct and balance a 10-ton bicycle? We should consult Nature.

Davidson responded to Pilcher's remarks with the comment that he used the term *lifter* because it was "suggestive of the distinction between the propellers to lift vertically as compared to those intended to drive horizontally." "As to the size of the machine, he came to the conclusion, after much consideration, that it was better to make it very large, else the carrying power was so small. He had been consulting Nature for the last 16 years, but now had come the time for consulting engineers, though he found it rather more expensive."[19]

Once again the proponents of large and small aircraft were in confrontation, but the argument was unresolved. Both were firm in their respective convictions, and both would follow their own paths.

On July 19 Wilson and Pilcher's secretary wrote to Chanute, enclosing two photographs to replace those lost in the post.[20] These pictures were almost certainly those taken in 1897 depicting Pilcher flying the Hawk under tow from "The Knob" at Upper Austin Lodge. Both survive in the front of Chanute's scrapbook of "Materials for the Study of the Aeronautical Experiments of Percy S. Pilcher,"

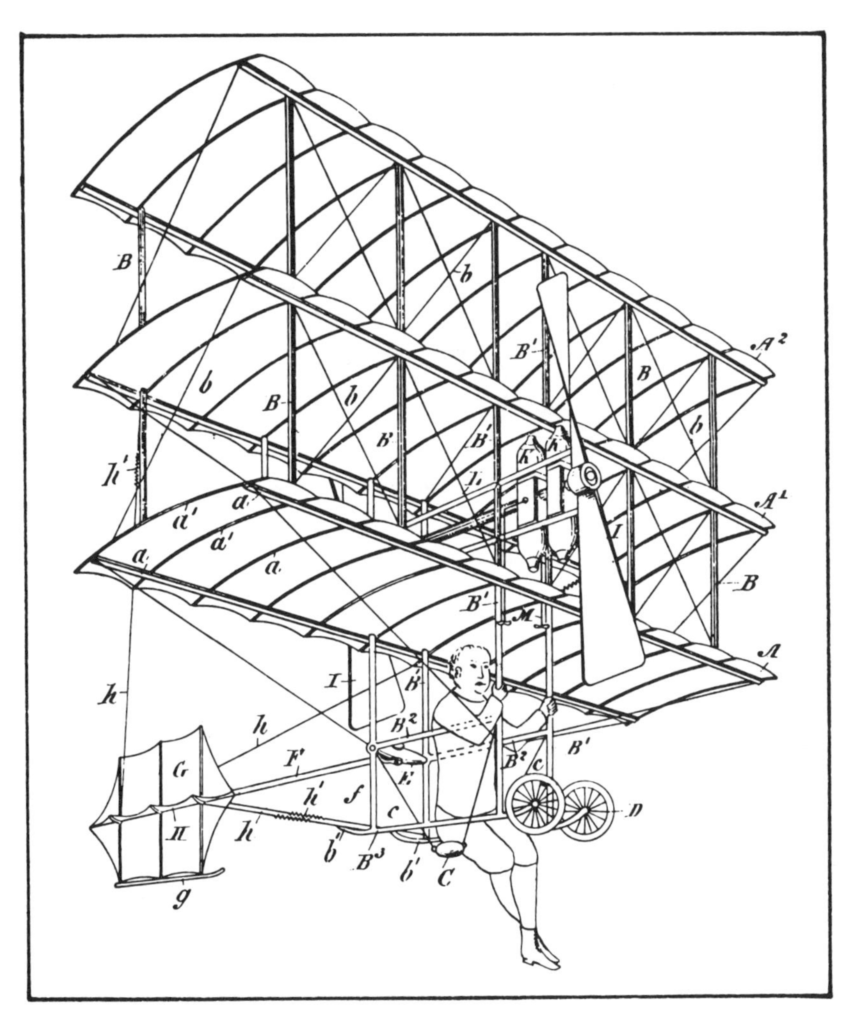

Although Herring's original application was rejected in the United States, the Chanute-Herring jointly filed patent for a powered triplane was accepted in Britain and France in the name of Thomas Moy. This illustration from the patent clearly shows the layout, with contrarotating tractor and pusher propellers in tandem. (Controller of Her Majesty's Stationery Office)

now in the Joseph Regenstein Library, University of Chicago Library. Both pictures are inscribed, in Pilcher's handwriting, "O. Chanute Esq. with Messrs. Wilson & Pilcher's Compliments."

American historians have stated that Herring's attempts to patent his powered triplane were unsuccessful.[21] This is not entirely true. In fact, although his application to the U.S. Patent Office was rejected in January 1898 because the machine had not demonstrated "proof of practical usefulness,"[22] it was accepted by the British Patent Office. The patent, now taken out jointly by Chanute and Herring, was communicated to the aforementioned Thomas Moy and was filed in Moy's name. It was applied for on June 25, 1897, and accepted on July 25, 1898, as No. 15,221 of 1897.[23] It is impossible to know when Pilcher first learned of this patent. As a prominent member of the ASGB, he must have known Moy, and, as we have seen, Moy discussed powered machines with him at the ASGB meeting of December 16, 1897, when the patent was being processed.[24] There is every possibility, therefore, that Moy had drawn it to his attention at that time, or even earlier. If not, Pilcher would probably have learned of it soon after its acceptance. The patent was also accepted in France.

Chanute and Herring's triplane had a wheeled chassis (mainly for ground handling), a cruciform tail with "gust-damping" springs incorporated in its bracing, a sling seat for the pilot beneath the lower mainplane, and a pair of single-cylinder "gasolene" or oil or gas engines, each driving an airscrew, one a tractor in front of the wings, the other a contrarotating pusher behind the wings. The engines, shafts, and propellers were mounted between the center and lower wings. As Pilcher was already converted to multiplanes by Chanute's successes, we can be sure that this patent would have provided further encouragement to follow this path.

Chanute wrote to Percy on August 5:[25]

> I beg to thank you for the two photographs of your machine in flight, which I have now received, together with your letter of July 19th.
>
> I had hoped to be able to send you a photo of Mr. Herring's motor machine, but he is making some changes in it, and has not yet tested it in flight.
>
> Have you found the plan of hauling the apparatus through the air with a line to give satisfaction in practice? I have been apprehensive lest

a misunderstanding of instructions or signals might lead to an accident, yet when hills are not convenient I see great advantages in the string.

With best respects

Pilcher apparently did not reply to this letter. Herring's "changes" to his powered glider, and trouble with the engine that powered his compressor, were not sorted out until October. Finally, on October 10 at St. Joseph, Michigan, the American managed a 50-foot powered hop into a 20-mile-per-hour wind (skids replaced the wheels during flight trials). His fragile aircraft had demonstrated its ability to move into the wind under power. Chanute came from Chicago on the 11th, hoping to see a flight, but the wind had dropped and no flights could be made. Not until late October were conditions again favorable, but on the morning of October 22 Herring managed a low flight of 73 feet into a 26-mile-per-hour wind, at a ground speed of perhaps only 5 or 6 miles per hour (an airspeed of about 32 miles per hour). He was pleased, but obviously realized that more power was needed and announced that he would build an improved machine to test in the coming spring. By that time his waning confidence was shattered when fire swept through his workshop, destroying his work. The improved machine was never built.[26]

Wilson and Pilcher's Mount Pleasant works were proving too cramped, and the company moved to larger premises at 32 & 34 Great Peter Street, Westminster, on December 8, 1898.[27] Business was evidently looking up. Shortly afterward Pilcher received a letter from the journalist Alex McCallum, who inquired as to the progress of aeronautical experiments over the past year. Pilcher replied on December 15:[28]

I do not know of anything of particular interest having happened in regard to flying this year—I have not yet seen the new *Aeronautical Annual,* I do not know if it has been published [the 1897 edition was the third and last]—I have heard that Herring and Chanute have been making experiments with a compressed air motor in one of the gliding machines—but I have not heard with what result—

I have not been able to make any experiments myself out of doors but we have been making an oil engine suitable for one of our soaring machines and which we hope to attach to one next spring and with which we trust real flight will be possible—

Augustus Moore Herring demonstrates the pilot's flying position in his powered hang glider, tested at St. Joseph, Michigan, in October 1898 with a small degree of success. The wheels were replaced by skids for the flight trials. The fan-type propellers are typical of the period, and Pilcher's would have been very similar. (E. E. Husting)

The *Aeronautical Annual* is sold by Wesley & Son Essex St. Strand so you can ask if it is out yet—

With very kind regards

While he had done no gliding at all in 1898, Pilcher had been active in other respects. One task that had been undertaken was the "reconstruction" of the Hawk. This is revealed in a letter to the magazine *Flight* from Mr. Laurence W. Miller of Calexico, California.[29] Miller was apparently an employee of the Wilson and Pilcher company, for he states: "I worked on the reconstruction of his machine for a year previous to his accident [in 1899], and made under his directions the biplane type of machine which he was to have tried on the day he met his death."

In view of its rough usage over two seasons, it is hardly surprising that the Hawk needed rebuilding, and we can be fairly certain that the patched wing fabric would have been completely replaced.

Miller's reference to a "biplane" is undoubtedly a confused recollection of Pilcher's final machine, a triplane, and the evolution of this

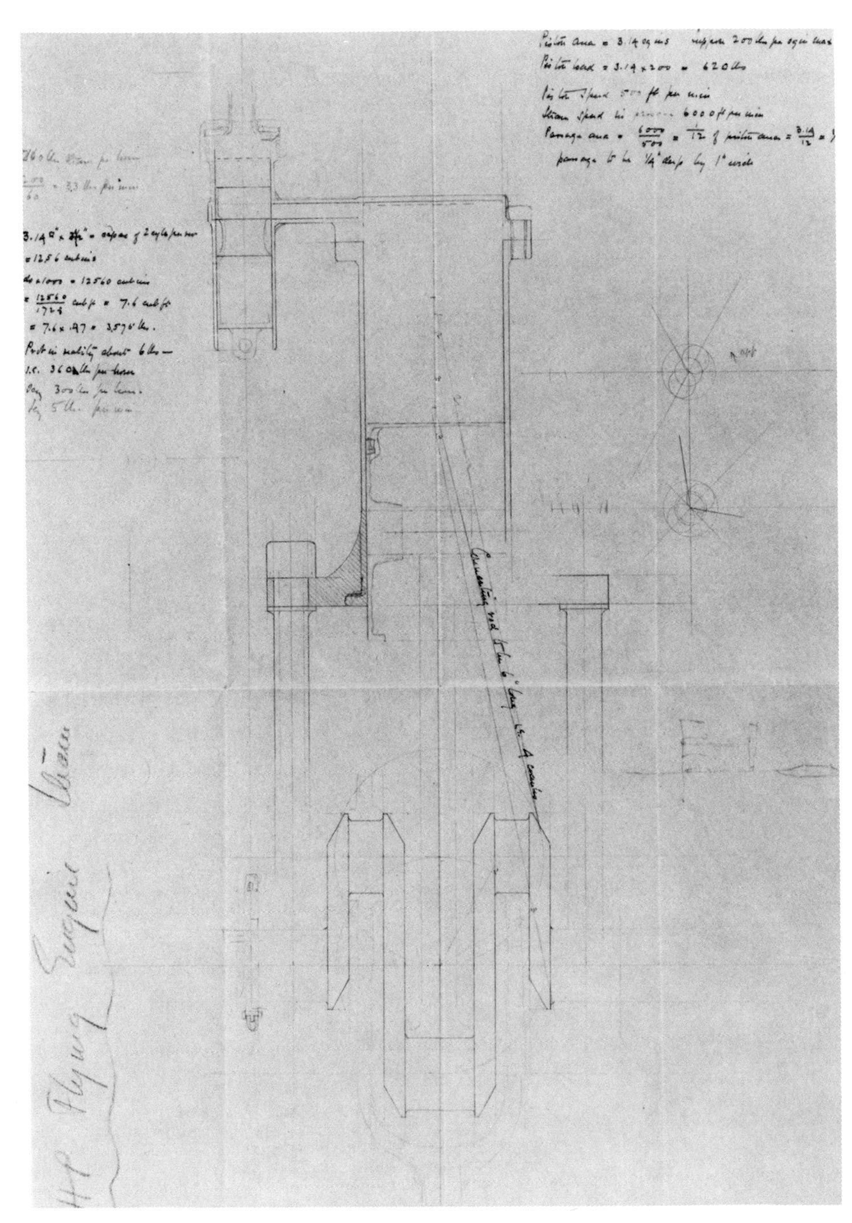

A drawing by Pilcher for a 4-horsepower two-cylinder horizontally opposed steam engine. To the right of the main drawing is the small doodle that was worked up into the unbuilt Duck quadruplane design.

design can be traced back to 1898. Two drawings by Pilcher survive that probably date from this year, which was marked by a fresh bout of designing.

The first drawing is a full-scale sectioned diagram, annotated by Pilcher, of a 4-horsepower steam engine (see p.109).[30] His figures, scribbled on the drawing, show that the engine used (in theory) 200 pounds of steam per hour—3.3 pounds per minute—and that two cylinders had a capacity of 12.56 cubic inches per revolution (7.6 cubic feet = 3.575 pounds), "Prob. in reality about 6 lbs.—i.e. 360 lbs. per hour. Say 300 lbs. per hour. Say 5 lbs. per min." Piston area was 3.14 square inches, piston speed 500 feet per minute, and the connecting rod was to be 6 inches long. The engine is of the two-cylinder, horizontally opposed type favored by Pilcher.

Of particular interest, however, is a small doodle on the right of the drawing. This is a side elevation of a powered quadruplane hang glider, with a pusher propeller driven by a long shaft from a motor positioned between the second and third wings, and a hexagonal tailplane. It is the barest of sketches, but is clearly the beginning of a tinted, half-inch-to-the-foot three-view drawing now in the Royal Aeronautical Society's library.[31]

This drawing reveals how greatly Chanute's multiplane had affected Pilcher's thinking. The quadruplane bears no resemblance whatsoever to its predecessors. Its "fuselage" comprises a simple rectangular frame 19 feet long and 2 feet wide. Laid across the rear is a kite-like hexagonal tailplane having a 4-foot span and two 2-foot-high vertical fins, one on each "longeron," strongly reminiscent of the upper vertical tail surface of the Chanute-Herring biplane glider. These provided ample fin area while avoiding the need for vertical surfaces below the tailplane, where they would have been prone to damage. The lowest wing spar was attached directly to the mainframe, and four vertical struts, 7 feet apart, linked it with the spars of the other three wings. The two inner vertical struts extended below the structure, and centers drawn beneath them suggest that wheels would have been fitted at their bottom ends. The gap between the wings was 2 feet.

The wing design was most unusual. The two upper wings were each divided into three panels comprising a center section and two outer panels of greater span at the leading edges. Each panel had three ribs, making a total of nine ribs to each three-panel wing, the ribs

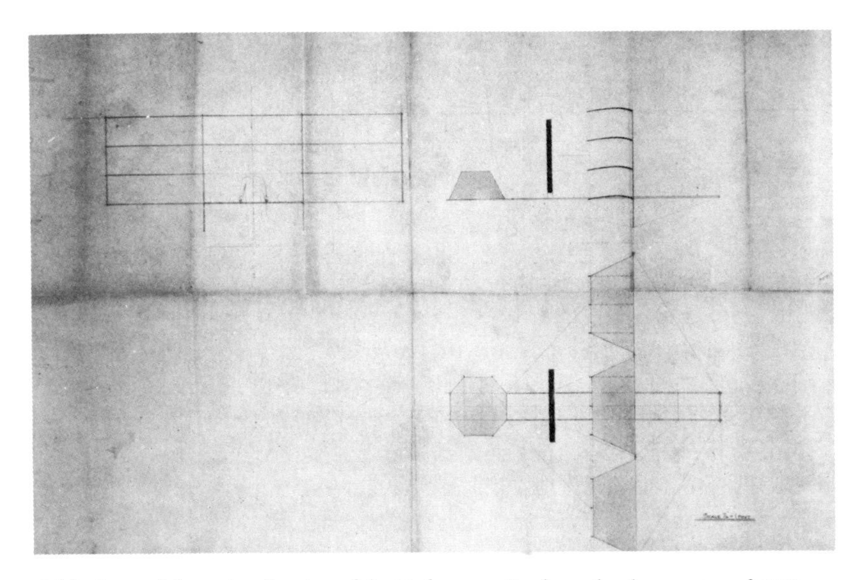

Pilcher's tinted three-view drawing of the 21-foot-span Duck quadruplane project of 1898. The vertical black line behind the wing trailing edges is the pusher propeller. Its shaft passed between the center two wings to an engine mounted on the front of the fuselage booms. The influence of the Chanute quadruplane and biplane gliders is obvious. (RAeS)

being anchored to the single spar, which also formed the wing leading edge. Chord was 3 feet, and the wings spanned 21 feet. There were large V-shaped cutouts between the panels, and it seems possible that these were originally provided to allow the outer panels to swing back against elastic restraints, as suggested in Chanute's multiplane patent, to absorb disturbing gusts. As the pilot was positioned where the central wing panels would be in the two lower wings, with his forearms resting on the mainframe longerons, only the outer panels were provided. Thus there was a total of ten wing panels, giving a total wing area of 165 square feet.

A 5-foot-diameter, two-bladed propeller is shown positioned above the mainframe and behind the wing cellule, its centerline passing above the pilot's head. This indicates that Pilcher had again opted for a long driveshaft, for to balance the aircraft the engine would have to have been mounted at the front of the mainframe, which extends well forward of the wings. The structure of the quadruplane is extremely sparse and light, and would therefore have required extensive bracing. However, only some basic wiring is indicated on the drawing. It must be remembered that, at the low speeds at which this aircraft would have flown, and because Pilcher's control system ruled out a larger machine, the drag penalty of numerous bracing wires was preferable to the weight penalty of a beefier structure.

Apparently the quadruplane was to be called the "Duck"—presumably because the long fuselage frame protruding forward of the wings was reminiscent of the "long-necked" appearance of a duck in flight. (Hence, also, the term *canard,* used to describe tail-first aircraft.) Notes made by J. E. Hodgson in the 1920s of material then in the possession of Percy's sister Ella[32] list a "Plan of the 'Duck'(?)—scale ½" = 1 foot." As the scale matches that of the quadruplane drawing, it is most probable that they are one and the same drawing. In a letter to Hodgson dated April 8, 1925,[33] Ella stated simply that "The Duck never materialised." This statement, too, accords with known facts. Although it is known that work on the engine was underway in 1898, it seems unlikely that construction of the new glider was started, for its configuration was to change somewhat during the next year.

Nonetheless, there can be little doubt that, aerodynamically, the new wings represented an improvement over those of the Hawk. Their greatly reduced chord and the use of ribs to maintain the curvature would have made them more efficient, though the V cutouts reduced the total area and would have reduced the lifting capability of the wing.

On December 17 Percy wrote to Baden-Powell,[34] drawing attention to the company's new address and stating that the firm had "just got possession of our new place here, but the place is still upside down." In the same month a printed letter concerning the move was produced on the Wilson and Pilcher letterhead:

> Dear Sir,
>
> We beg to inform you that we are now in occupation of the NEW PREMISES as above, which we have recently erected and fitted out as an Engineering Workshop, for the execution of work of a moderate size.
>
> Our shops are so arranged as to facilitate the handling of work of as varied a nature as possible, with a view principally to the working out of new designs and inventions, which, as heretofore, will form our special line of business.
>
> In addition to a Machine Shop, which is equipped with the newest tools, we have a large Wood-working Shop and extensive Drawing

Office; while a considerable space remains available for, and is devoted to, Mechanical and Electrical experiments.

Hoping that you may find an opportunity of visiting our New Works, over which we shall take great pleasure in showing you,

We are, dear Sir,
Yours faithfully,
WILSON & PILCHER LTD.

Pilcher sent copies of this letter both to Chanute and to Lawrence Hargrave in Australia. On Chanute's copy he penned the footnote: "I hope you will keep us advised of what you are doing with your flying experiments—we were able to do nothing this last year—through want of leisure—PSP."[35] The footnote on Hargrave's copy reads: "I'm still experimenting with the wings—& will try & let you know the results from time to time. Yrs PSP."[36]

The year 1898 concludes with a letter of which the original can no longer be traced. In the "Memoir" in the front of the ASGB's *Aeronautical Classics No. 5—Gliding by Percy S. Pilcher,* published in 1910, editors T. O'B. Hubbard and J. H. Ledeboer quote from a letter that Percy wrote to Professor Fitzgerald of Dublin "at the end of 1898":

> During the last year I was not able to do anything with the flying work, as we were so very busy getting our new business into going order; but the summer before, when I was able to devote some time to it, the results we obtained were most encouraging, and consequently we are most anxious not to let the experiments drop altogether. In America experiments are continually being made, and it would be heartrending not to try and keep one's place in the work that is being done.

With the Hawk re-covered and a new engine and a new glider on the way, Percy was clearly anticipating an eventful year ahead.

5

A Very Bad Business, 1899

Octave Chanute replied to Pilcher's printed letter on January 8 of the new year:[1]

> I have your recent favour, but, like yourself, I have been able to do no experimenting during the past year, having been absorbed by business matters.
>
> I have however arranged for some experiments on automatic stability, which are to be carried out by a former assistant of Prof. Langley, who finds himself at leisure [this was Edward Huffaker, who had resigned from the Smithsonian Institution in December 1898, and was to work on a new biplane glider incorporating the swinging-wing system[2]]. I have also written an article for *McClure's Magazine,*[3] and another for the Strasbourg *Illustri[e]rte Aeronautische Mittheilingen* [*sic*][4] which I presume will appear in due time. I shall always be glad to hear from you.

Despite his preoccupation with aeronautics, Pilcher still worked on other inventions. On January 17 Wilson and Pilcher filed a joint patent, No. 1100, for "Electric Light Brackets." The exact nature of these devices remains obscure, because the application was abandoned.[5]

If there was any chance that Percy was still unaware of the Moy-Chanute-Herring powered triplane patent, then he would have found reference to it in the list of "Applications for patents" in the *Aeronautical Journal* for January 1899, where the multiplane patent was also listed. This issue also contained a short article on Lawrence Hargrave's "soaring kites," of which more will be heard later.[6]

At this time Pilcher was still without a place to fly his gliders. After the loss of the Eynsford site shared with Maxim, he had found no time to fly anyway, but he was now seeking a suitable site from which to resume his trials. On January 30 he wrote to Baden-Powell, sympathizing with him on the parlous state of the finances of the *Aeronautical Journal.*[7] Baden-Powell, an enthusiastic designer and flyer of kites, had obviously suggested that the society could start a kite club that would have its own "flying ground." As he, too, would have been able to use such a site for his gliding experiments, Pilcher seemed keen; "Do you think the Society will really think of starting a camp & a club house?" he asked. Percy concluded, "I am now hunting the flat parts of Kent for suitable places—I was at Sandwich on Sunday [the 29th], that is far but is the very best place I have ever seen."

The reference to "flat parts of Kent" is interesting, as it shows that he wished to fly from the level, either under tow or by power.

It was probably at about this time that Wilson and Pilcher drafted a "preliminary circular" for a syndicate to finance their further work toward powered flight. An undated carbon copy of this document survives in the Royal Aeronautical Society's library:

> *32 and 34, Great Peter Street,* WESTMINSTER
>
> Increased attention has recently been paid to the subject of aerial navigation both by the public and by scientific men, of whom several, both in Europe and America, are actively engaged in studying the conditions of artificial flight.
>
> Broadly speaking, the practical solution of the problem has been approached from two different points of view, the one represented perhaps chiefly by Mr. Maxim, who has especially directed his attention to the construction of a machine capable of lifting itself; the other by the late Herr Lilienthal who, despite his ultimate disaster, which cost him his life successfully demonstrated the feasibility of balancing in the air a gliding apparatus, to which eventually propelling machinery might be applied.
>
> Among the several experimenters who have adopted Herr Lilienthal's line of procedure as probably the more likely to be fruitful of result is Mr. Percy Pilcher who, both in consultation with Herr Lilienthal and since his decease, has conducted many similar experiments with improved apparatus in this country. Enclosed with this circular is an

extract from "Nature" descriptive of one of the most successful of his experiments, together with two photographs of the machine used on the occasion.

Besides the practical experience obtained through these experiments in soaring, lasting over more than three years, Mr. Pilcher has an extensive knowledge of mechanical engineering and has also had the advantage of working with Mr. Maxim for a considerable time upon his flying machine, and he is thoroughly conversant with the most recent experiments in this direction and their results.

About a year ago, in conjunction with Mr. W. G. Wilson, B.A. 1st Class Mechanical science Tripos Cantab. he established under the name of Wilson and Pilcher Limited, a business for the carrying out of experimental engineering work.

Mr. Pilcher having succeeded in learning how to handle a gliding machine in the air and to make safe landings, it remained to construct an engine to maintain it in continuous flight. The firm of Wilson and Pilcher, Ltd., have accordingly recently been engaged in producing a light oil engine suitable for this purpose, and this engine is now approaching completion.

Although the soaring experiments have claimed a great deal of time and personal attention, the actual out of pocket expenses have been comparatively small but a stage has now been reached when, in order to be able to carry the matter to a successful issue, Mr. Pilcher finds himself obliged to seek some financial support.

In inviting co-operation in the syndicate which it is proposed to form, it must be understood that the enterprise is not represented to be other than of a purely experimental and speculative character, and Mr. Pilcher is especially anxious not to be counted among the many enthusiastic inventors who confidently claim to be on the point of achieving an immediate triumph when they have really barely touched the fringe of the difficulties which beset the subject.

It is felt, however, that there should be several willing to risk a small sum of money in an undertaking which, while in any event of the highest mechanical interest, may not improbably prove to be of very great commercial value. Now, in point of fact, Mr. Pilcher has practically mastered what appears to be the chief difficulty, that of balance; while, in the particular experiment referred to above, and others of a similar nature, he has ascertained that the necessary motive power is such as can be derived from an engine which could easily be carried on the machine.

The cost of each completed apparatus should not exceed £300, but in order to leave a margin for experiment it is considered that a capital of £2,000 should be available to be called on if required during the space of 3 or 4 years.

It is proposed therefore that a Syndicate be formed with a total capital of £4,000, of which £2,000 shall be issued in cash and £2,000 allotted in shares to Wilson and Pilcher, Limited, by whom the engine and all existing apparatus shall be assigned to the Syndicate at the price of £100. The Directors are to be elected by the shareholders, and to have the power of governing the general course of experiments; and the majority of the subscribers to the Syndicate, if at any time dissatisfied with what is being done, shall have the power, on paying expenses up to date, to close the enterprise and cancel their liability on all uncalled capital. The voting power of the Shareholders to be proportioned to the amount of their subscriptions.

In consideration for their share of the Syndicate, Messrs. Wilson and Pilcher Limited will be prepared to execute all work in connection with the undertaking in their newly equipped workshops at 32 and 34 Great Peter Street, Westminster, at cost price. The exact meaning of this term being decided from time to time by the Directors.

It is proposed to make a call of 5/- in the £1 as soon as the Syndicate is formed and registered,: this should suffice for all work during the summer. All calls will be made by the Directors.

The following gentlemen have signified their intention to subscribe and authorize the use of their names on the present circular.

[A space is left here for the list of names.]

NOTE:
Subscriptions to the present preliminary circular are conditional upon approval of the Articles of Association, which will be drafted as soon as it is seen that the Syndicate is likely to meet with a satisfactory measure of support.[8]

Several interesting points emerge from this document. First, Percy regarded the demonstration at Upper Austin Lodge on June 20, 1897, described in *Nature,* as "one of the most successful of his experiments." Secondly, he optimistically claimed to have "succeeded in learning how to handle a gliding machine in the air and to make safe landings," and to have "practically mastered . . . the chief difficulty, that of balance," though his weight-shift control system severely restricted the size of the aircraft, and he was fully aware of this and knew the dilemma that faced him when the weight of an engine was added. However, he was clearly not deluded into overconfidence, as he did not "claim to be on the point of achieving an immediate triumph," and realized that he had "barely touched the fringe of the difficulties which beset the subject."

Wilson and Pilcher obviously hoped to be appointed directors of the syndicate. Had they not been so appointed, they would have relinquished any control over the direction that the experiments took. However, the power of the subscribers to withdraw their support if they were disappointed with the work could also have restricted them; but a compromise had to be made in order to gain the financial support that would enable their work to continue.

Baden-Powell was a recipient of one of these circulars, for Pilcher wrote to him on February 9 in reply to a letter written a week earlier:[9]

> Many thanks for your letter of Feb 2nd. I'm very glad you are going to put your self down for the Flying Syndicate—you can tell me how much later on—Can you get some other people interested in it?
>
> I'm very sorry you have got so much out of pocket over the Journal & trust you will get paid back in time—I'm afraid Hurlingham or a place like that would not do for the Club—Horses & kites don't agree—& any gear left at a place like that would be sure to get smashed up.
>
> With regard to your questions about the Syndicate—Yes the shares are £1 each—Wilson & Pilcher Ltd. are given £2,000 in *shares* (not cash) which they *may not* sell—All they receive in money is £100 for the Engine & gear of which there is a lot.

Regrettably, we have no means of knowing how much support the syndicate gained, although it was stated in the *Rugby Advertiser* for October 7, 1899, that Pilcher "was supported by a number of scientific men, who had formed a small syndicate to help him in his investigations,"[10] and it is known that Ella had a copy of the prospectus in the 1920s, which included a list of subscribers, among them "F. Elgar £100, Prof. G. F. Fitzgerald £25, and J. Dunn £50."[11]

The "light oil engine" that was "approaching completion" also remains enigmatic, as no drawings or photographs of it exist. Designed by Walter Wilson, it was air-cooled, weighed 40 pounds, and had cast bronze cylinders and pistons made from solid steel forgings. One of Wilson's sons, A. G. Wilson, has stated that the two cylinders were set opposite one another "in the same fashion that my father designed the 4-cylinder and 6-cylinder Wilson-Pilcher motor-car engines."[12] Some impression of its appearance can be gained by looking at the four-cylinder engine used in the Wilson-Pilcher car of 1901. The cylinders had water-jacketed heads and air-cooled fins, and had a bore of 3 inches and a 3-inch stroke. The crankcase was enclosed. This motor produced only about 5 horsepower at 1,000 revolutions per minute.[13] The engine for the new glider would probably have resembled a smaller, two-cylinder version of this motor, and may therefore have been underpowered. However, the water-cooled four-cylinder engine of the 1903 Wilson-Pilcher car, which had an open crankcase, produced a healthy 10 horsepower, and the six-cylinder version of 1904 gave 18–24 horsepower.[14] All of the car engines were noted for their smooth running.

Another patent was applied for by Wilson and Pilcher on February 22. Numbered 3941, it was for "wheels," but whether the wheels in question were for automobiles or flying machines remains unknown, as this patent was also abandoned.[15]

On April 10 one of Pilcher's distant correspondents arrived in England. Lawrence Hargrave brought his family, "some large kites, a kit of tools and my manuscript notes" from Australia in the hope of obtaining assistance with his own flying-machine experiments in the country of his birth.[16] Disillusionment came quickly when he realized that "my available means are inadequate to meet the style my party are accustomed to and I must either curtail my visit or convert what I had intended to be a pleasure trip for my wife and daughters into a disheartening toil for them." The family took rooms at 12 Gillingham Street, London SW, close to Victoria Station, and Hargrave "Had a long yarn with Pilcher at his new shop." He added: "Pilcher thinks no one is working on aviation with any enthusiasm."[17] Things were certainly very quiet. Chanute and Herring had done nothing since 1897 and 1898, respectively, Europe was silent, Maxim had ceased work, and Pilcher must have felt quite alone in the field at this time. Of Baden-Powell, Wilson, and Pilcher, Hargrave later wrote, "They are about the best fellows I know, and all are busy men."[18] Only two weeks after his arrival in England, Hargrave decided to return to Australia in June. Before his departure, however, he was to address the ASGB, at Baden-Powell's request, on Friday, May 26.

Meanwhile another patent for "wheels"—No. 10,589—was filed by Pilcher and Wilson on May 19. Like its predecessor of three months earlier, this, too, was abandoned and remains vague.[19]

The "soaring kite" that Hargrave presented to the Aeronautical Society in May 1899. (RAeS)

The ASGB meeting on the evening of May 26 was held at the Society of Arts, Adelphi. There was a "large attendance," and much interest was shown in Hargrave's kites and model soaring machine, which were on show in the hall. The meeting was chaired by Pilcher, who introduced his friend in glowing terms: "Mr. Hargrave has lately obtained some most wonderful results. I am glad he has photographs with him, otherwise we should have great difficulty in believing some of the startling facts which he will tell us."[20]

Hargrave then proceeded to describe the kites that he had brought with him. He built them of "Oregon" (pine) covered with Calico. "Much praise has been lavished on bamboo," he stated, "but I have never seen a sample that I would work into a kite." After describing the construction, operation, and dismantling of his box kites, he turned to his latest device, a "soaring kite." This kite bore no resemblance to his famous cellular kites, but was more like a model glider in appearance. It comprised a solid wooden wing of cambered, airfoil section (which Hargrave called the "propeller"), a dependent lead weight that could be adjusted fore and aft, and a vertical tail that "acts only as a weather cock." Both monoplane and biplane versions had been tested. To avoid damage, Hargrave had hung the kites from a cord stretched between two posts 24 feet high and 48 feet apart. He claimed that the soaring kite on show, when correctly ballasted, would "ascend slowly at an angle of 45° to windward" in a wind of 12 to 14 miles per hour and loaded at 1.78 pounds per square foot. "With a wind velocity of about 17 miles per hour, and a load of 2.13 lbs. per square foot, it will rise to an angle of 70° or 80° to windward," he stated.

The paper was well received and drew lengthy discussion, with Maxim holding forth at some length and both Archibald and Davidson participating. The discussion centered on the performance of the soaring kite, and members attempted to explain its behavior. One suggested that the kite soared because it was in an ascending wind. Hargrave's reply, that he "thought it best to pass over any remarks that had been made about an ascending tend in the wind, because in an ascending current, almost anything can be done," hid the fact that he seems not to have checked on wind elevation at all.[21]

Pilcher announced that "Mr. Hargrave has most kindly given the whole of the kites [six cellular kites and a soaring machine] to Captain Baden-Powell, and he, in turn, has made them a present to the Society, and they will be available, some day or other, for anybody to come and look at and measure up—I believe even to practise with."

Thanking Hargrave for his "most interesting paper," Pilcher added: "I think the best thing that can be done, since Mr. Hargrave has given his collection of kites to the Society, will be for the Society to try and subscribe enough funds to found a clubhouse somewhere out of London at which experiments can be made, and where the Society can store any flying apparatus (which is occasionally rather a white elephant) or anything else that may be made, and where members can go and try experiments with the models and things which others have made. I believe you will hear further from the Secretary as to this."[22]

Percy was still seeking a base for his own homeless gliders, and on June 9 he wrote to Baden-Powell suggesting locations for the Kite Club:

> Dear Baden Powell
>
> I am returning the photographs as you ask—How do you think Taplow [Buckinghamshire] would do for the Kite Flying Club House?

We could get a nice plot on the river there quite cheap—on a short lease—I believe we could get a couple of acres subject to a 6 months notice to quit—at £2 an acre a year—

Or would you prefer to use Dorney Common [also in Bucks] and get quite a small piece for a home alongside the common—the country is very open about there—its [*sic*] handy to get at—and it would be very handy for you would it not.

Yrs
P. S. Pilcher

Do you think we could borrow £200 or £300 for the building? Or do you think we could borrow some £500 to buy the ground the club house would stand on, build a nice brick house, and then there would be some security for the money.[23]

In spite of Percy's enthusiasm, the Kite Flying Club was never established. It was not until 1909 that the ASGB acquired its own flying ground, and even then it proved a sad failure.[24]

Hargrave and his family left England on June 23 and returned to Sydney, where he resumed his lonely research.

At some time during June and July Pilcher found a home for the Hawk. His friends, having failed to deter Percy from his dangerous pursuit, decided that his experiments should be continued at a site where his gliders could be properly cared for, where the ground was suitable for flying, and where assistance would be at hand in case of accident. The Honorable Adrian Verney Cave (later the 6th Lord Braye) therefore arranged for the glider to be stored at the Braye family home at Stanford Hall, near Rugby, where Wilson and Pilcher had first met. "There was the probability," reported the *Rugby Advertiser* for October 7, 1899, "that if the 5th Lord Braye refused to permit the experiments to be carried on in his demesne, Mr. Pilcher would only seek some other spot in which the ascents would be surrounded by more danger."

On July 25 Pilcher wrote to Baden-Powell:

Will the Society lend me a few kites for a few weeks—One moderate rigid Hargrave will do well to start with—I want to fly them at Stanford Park near Rugby where the soaring machine now is—If you can spare one will you kindly send it here [Great Peter Street] or say if I may send for it—If you would sooner wait till after Friday please say so

& I will bring away the kite on Friday night—I presume they will be on show there.[25]

The reference to Friday concerns an ASGB meeting at the Society of Arts on July 26. However, Baden-Powell seems to have sent the keys to the box of kites straight away, for a scribbled note at the foot of the letter reads: "Certainly—send keys herewith of box at Soc. of Arts."

Percy is reported to have made "several successful flights" in the Hawk during July, August, and September, "whilst staying from time to time at Stanford Hall"—four flights is the number stated in one reference.[26] It was said that on several occasions "he had made flights of 300 or 400 yards at an altitude of from 20 ft. to 50 ft."[27] The Honorable Adrian Verney Cave also made several flights on the Hawk under Pilcher's guidance.[28] A popular story told by the present Lord Braye relates that on one occasion his grandfather returned from London to find some forty members of the Stanford Hall staff pulling on the line to launch Percy into the air. That evening at dinner he tactfully suggested that perhaps twenty men would have been enough, as no milking had been done at the local farms. Bearing in mind that three boys had been sufficient to launch Percy in 1897 using his pulley system, even twenty seems an extremely large number.[29]

During August the first tests of the engine took place, and several successful bench runs were made.[30] Pilcher had also developed a "specially designed dynamometer for gauging the thrust of the propeller, which was quite a departure from the form used by Mr. Maxim."[31]

Meanwhile, Percy had persisted "with considerable success"[32] in his attempts to persuade well-known engineers, scientific men, and wealthy and influential people to finance his experiments. One such person, who obviously showed keen interest, was John Henniker Heaton, the Conservative member of Parliament for Canterbury (later Sir John Henniker Heaton Bart). Henniker Heaton championed the cause of improved communications, coining the slogan "Make the communications between our coasts as easy as speech and as free as air," and in 1898 he had played a major role in the introduction of Imperial Penny Postage. A later print entitled "Linking up the World" depicts him watching a host of small monoplanes representing countries linked with London, their wings bearing the words "London-America," "London-Africa," and so on. He clearly appreciated the potential of the airplane as a means of communication.[33]

Work on the new powered glider was also progressing well. No photographs are known to survive of this machine, but all contemporary eyewitness accounts describe it as a triplane, and we do have drawings and sketches of fragments with which to reconstruct its probable appearance.

In December of 1910 the British designer and builder of aircraft T. W. K. Clarke made detailed, dimensioned drawings of some of the surviving components of the triplane.

From these drawings we know that the triplane's wings closely resembled those shown in the 1898 quadruplane drawing in their design and construction, each being composed of a number of tapered panels. However, these panels were somewhat smaller than those of the quadruplane, spanning 5 feet 6 inches rather than 7 feet. Evidence strongly suggests that each wing was composed of four panels rather than the Duck's three, which would be a logical way of compensating for the reduction in wing area that resulted from the deletion of the topmost wing.

Clarke had two "sets" of two wing panels each, representing two half-wings, plus one single panel, from which to work. One of the two-panel "sets" had a spar of yellow pine; the other set had a spar of bamboo. This suggests that the spar of the lower wing, which was attached to the mainframe and took the stress from the wings above, was probably of pine, while the others were of bamboo to save weight. The ribs were of American elm or Kauri pine, and the fabric was thought to be a fine sailcloth. (Clarke suggested "Union Silk—Egyptian Cotton," but Percy's favorite—nainsook—seems just as likely.)[34]

Some of these fragments survived until at least 1959, when "pieces of material" from one of the wings were shown on a BBC television documentary.[35] They have since disappeared altogether, but an aeronautical designer-draftsman-illustrator, Mr. Ted Shreeve, who saw the remains in 1959, made sketches from memory for the author (see postscript).

Limitations were imposed on the design by the size of machine that Pilcher could handle. The wings had to span between 20 and 24 feet and have an area no greater than 170 square feet; the airframe had to weigh between 50 and 60 pounds and would have had to carry Pilcher, the new engine, and its propeller, for a total weight of about 206 pounds; thus the all-up weight was about 266 pounds. It would

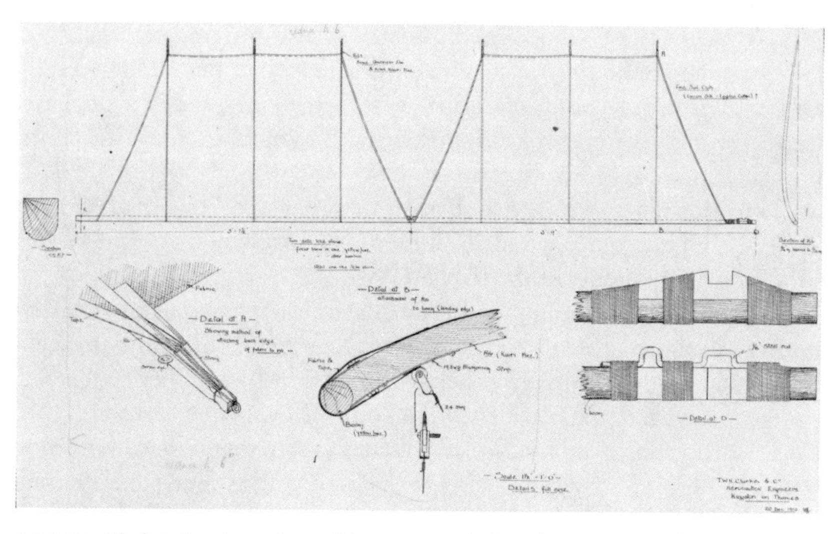

T. W. K. Clarke's drawings of two of the wing panels from the surviving triplane components, with details in larger scale below. The drawing is dated December 20, 1910. (RAeS)

have had to sustain itself at about 25–35 miles per hour. We can be quite sure that the engine installation would have followed that proposed in the patent for the powered Hawk and retained in the quadruplane drawing.

Using this information and the Clarke drawings, the author attempted in 1978 to recreate the triplane's likeness.[36] If four of the smaller wing panels were used, the total wing span came to 23 feet and the total wing area to 144 square feet—rather on the low side, but within requirements. With an arbitrary gap of 2 feet 6 inches between the wings, Pilcher's powerplant installation, translated directly from the patent and quadruplane drawings, fitted perfectly, with the long driveshaft to the pusher propeller passing just above the center wing. In assuming, logically, that the figure in the Duck drawing represents Pilcher himself (all of his gliders were, of course, "tailor made"), the author found that this same figure also fitted the triplane reconstruction perfectly—the figure's head was comfortably clear of the underside of the middle wing and his feet just right to enable him to stand with the glider's wheels lifted clear of the ground. It was assumed that, as in the Hawk, Pilcher would rest his forearms along the mainframe members and grasp short struts, and that small bolsters would be provided to support his shoulder blades.

The vertical struts linking the wings were fitted into notched pieces bound to the spars, as shown in Clarke's drawings. The spars themselves were only 3/4 inch in diameter, and the ribs were held to them by 19 swg aluminum strips. Fabric covered the top surface of the wings and continued round the leading edge and for a short distance beneath the wing. All edges were taped, and at the trailing edges the fabric was drawn tight by tape loops and string tensioners tied to screw eyes in the rib ends. Since extensive bracing would have been

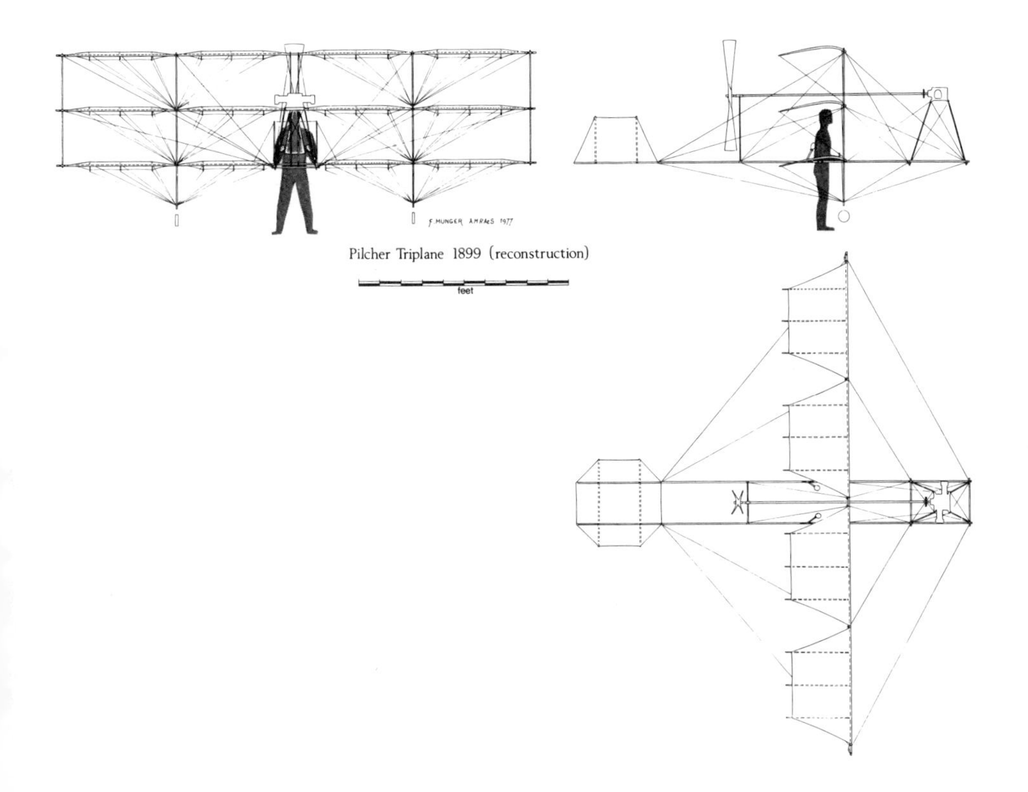

The probable configuration of Pilcher's last machine, the untested powered triplane of 1899. This "restoration" was developed from known details by the author and artist Frank Munger in 1977.

essential to make the structure rigid, screw eyes were provided in the tail of each rib, and anchorage points at the wing tips.

Historians have often stated that the triplane was the outcome of Percy's excitement over Hargrave's soaring kites.[37] This claim, however, was made in complete ignorance of the influential link between Pilcher and Chanute and the strong evidence it provides of the inspirational influence of the Chanute multiplane and biplane gliders. Moreover, the short amount of time between Hargrave's lecture and the completion of the triplane argues strongly against any influence from that direction, especially as the running of Wilson and Pilcher Limited was keeping both Pilcher and Wilson very busy, as evidenced by Percy's letters.

While his triplane was approaching completion, Percy arranged to give a gliding demonstration at Stanford Park. This was largely for the benefit of Henniker Heaton, for whom he "was very anxious to perform because Mr. Henniker Heaton had expressed great interest in the operations, and [Pilcher] wished to increase that interest," as Lord Braye later stated.[38] The date was set for Saturday, September 30, and the new triplane was to be displayed at the same time. It was an important event, because, according to later statements by John Hill, an engineer employed at Stanford Hall, and (probably) by the Honorable Everard Feilding, a close follower of Pilcher's experiments, it was to be the last experiment at Stanford Hall before the engine was fitted into a glider for experiments in "free flight" under power.[39]

A setback occurred shortly before the demonstration, when the engine suffered a broken crankshaft while being tuned up to give more power.[40] It would mean major repairs, but would not affect the forthcoming event.

On Saturday, September 23, Percy wrote to the Honorable Adrian Verney Cave on personal letterhead from Wilson and Pilcher's Great Peter Street works:

> Dear Cave,
>
> I have the new machine almost done & will try and have it up at Stanford by Friday—
>
> I will come by the 4 o'clock on Friday unless I hear from you to the contrary—
>
> Are the Axles & all ready & in place?
>
> *Yrs*
> *P. S. Pilcher*[41]

Artist Frank Munger's impression of Pilcher's powered triplane as it probably would have looked in flight.

The "Axles & all" refer to the line and pulley system for launching the Hawk from the level and towing it through the air.

On Thursday the 28th, John Hill and Verney Cave "thoroughly overhauled the machine" and "made more careful preparations than they had ever done previously."[42] All was ready for the big event two days hence.

Saturday, September 30, dawned dismally. It was stormy, and there were sundry heavy showers until 2:00 P.M., with a gusty wind blowing from the south-southwest. Frequent light showers persisted in the afternoon.[43]

The people present for the demonstration included "a number of county people, who took refuge under the trees." Those known to be there were Lord and Lady Braye; their eldest son, the Honorable Adrian Verney Cave; Percy's sister Ella; John Hill the engineer; the Honorable Everard Feilding, brother of Lord Denbigh; Col. B. F. S. Baden-Powell of the ASGB; Mr. Henniker Heaton M. P.; and Dr. Nash of Welford. Dr. Stewart was in Stanford Hall.

Pilcher, who had brought two assistants with him (one of whom was apparently Mr. Laurence W. Miller),[44] was anxious to perform for the benefit of Henniker Heaton. Several friends attempted to dissuade him from flying, but he stated that the wind was suitable. Both Verney Cave and Hill later agreed, Hill pointing out that a strong wind was in Pilcher's favor (flying into wind reduced his speed over the ground), and Verney Cave saying that Percy had flown on windier days.

The afternoon's proceedings began with some trials of the kites that Hargrave had presented to the ASGB. They are alleged to have been flown by one of Lord Braye's employees, a "resident engineer" named Peabody, who was Hill's assistant.[45] It was then decided to try some flights in the Hawk, and both this glider and the new triplane were brought out, the latter without its wing covering "spread."[46] The Hawk was to be towed aloft by a horse pulling on a "very light cotton line, perhaps 300 or 400 yards long,"[47] which was attached to the fall of a tackle with a purchase of four or five parts to multiply the speed of the horse and provide a steady pull. Verney Cave was "in charge of the traction power," assisted by John Hill and another Stanford Hall employee, named Tanser.[48]

Pilcher and Verney Cave gave the machine a careful preflight examination and ascertained that "everything was in perfect order." The first tow was started at 4:00 P.M., but once the glider had reached 30 feet the cord broke and Pilcher descended. The same happened on a second attempt,[49] and one account states that Pilcher remarked "that the rain had made the machine very heavy, and that it was difficult to get up the desired speed."[50] Another account says that "the performer expressed his doubts whether his machine would soar well on account of the saturation of the canvas wings."[51] Contradicting this, John Hill recalled that "The machine had been kept perfectly dry, and when the trial took place it was not raining."

Whatever the case, a third attempt was begun at about 4:20 P.M. and "Mr. Pilcher rose very well," traveling some 150 yards and reaching a height estimated variously at between 30 and 60 feet. Suddenly "a snap was heard," the Hawk's tail "was seen to collapse," and the glider somersaulted forward, its wings folding upward as it did so. The Honorable Adrian Verney Cave "let go the line," but it was to no avail; the Hawk "came down heavily . . . with a crash that could be heard some hundreds of yards,"[52] and with Pilcher underneath the wreckage. Laurence Miller recalled that Pilcher "fell practically at my feet."

Verney Cave ran to the site, closely followed by Percy's sister Ella and Everard Feilding. When Dr. Nash reached the scene of the accident, Pilcher had already been extricated from the wreckage, and was lying on his back unconscious, breathing very hard and moaning. "It was painfully evident," recalled Baden-Powell, "that his left leg was broken high up on the thigh, but no other traces of injury were apparent."[53] Lady Braye sent orders to Stanford Hall for blankets and warm water to be prepared, and Pilcher was lifted onto a shutter and carried into his room in the house. Here Dr. Nash, assisted by Dr. Stewart, examined Pilcher. He was found to be suffering from "very severe concussion, a fracture of the left thigh, and a fracture of the right shin bone."[54] Dr. Simpson of Rugby then arrived, and also Dr. Clement Dukes, and between them the four medical men set the fractures and made the patient "as comfortable as possible."

Later, as most of the visitors were returning to London, reassuring reports were issued, although Pilcher had still not regained consciousness. His condition was extremely critical. Telegrams had been dispatched to relations immediately after the disaster, and his brother, Lt. Col. Thomas Pilcher, still stationed in Dublin with the Bedfordshire Light Infantry, arrived in Rugby on the Sunday morning.[55] The Honorable Everard Feilding sent a full account of the accident to his brother Lord Denbigh, who was on duty as lord-in-waiting at Balmoral, "so that the Queen might be fully and privately informed, as she always likes to be."[56]

Pilcher lingered through Sunday, October 1, but finally succumbed to his injuries at 3:00 A.M. in the morning of Monday, October 2, some 34 hours after the accident, without regaining consciousness. Death was attributed to concussion of the brain and spine. He was thirty-two years old.

Mr. George Bouskell, the coroner for South Leicestershire, held an inquest in the large dining room at Stanford Hall on October 3. It had transpired that there was not a single qualified juryman in the Parish of Weston and Stanmore, in which Stanford Hall is situated. In fact, it was the only residence in the parish at that time. The jury therefore comprised Swinford residents, namely; the Reverend G. J. Powell (foreman), and Messrs. Chas. King, Thos. Gilbert, John Gilbert, J. Simons, J. R. Simons, R. Spencer, S. Matthews, B. Knight,

W. Berridge, T. W. Berridge, J. Smith, and T. M. Atkinson. Also present were Lord Braye and the Honorable Adrian Verney Cave, the Honorable Everard Feilding, Colonel Pilcher, and Dr. Stewart.

The first to testify was Verney Cave, who identified the body and gave a brief outline of the deceased's career, stating that Pilcher's lodgings had been at 15 Lincoln Street, Queen's Road, London. He described the circumstances of the accident and recalled the final stages thus:

> Something seemed to go wrong with the rudder, and witness saw the cross-bar of the machine snap, whereupon the wings collapsed, and the machine came to the ground. In witnesses' opinion the cause of the collapse was the snapping of the cross-bar. He saw Mr. Pilcher give a jerk, and that seemed too much for the machine.

Three points should be noted—the failure in the "rudder" refers to the "horizontal rudder," or tailplane; he *saw* the crossbar snap; and he *saw* Pilcher give a jerk. The significance of these observations will be seen later. Verney Cave stated that he had examined the remains of the Hawk, but had been unable to determine what had caused the "rudder" to fail. He opined that one of the lines from the kingposts to the tail, which ensured that the negative incidence of the latter was retained, had given way.

At this point several members of the jury, being unfamiliar with the design or appearance of the glider, expressed a wish to see it. They adjourned to the shed where the Hawk lay, "apparently just as brought in, its white canvas sails, damp and soiled, resembling a huge flat umbrella." Alongside, suspended from a beam, hung "another huge canvas kite-like thing" (presumably a Hargrave box kite), and under a nearby gateway was the new and untested triplane, "with triple sails on either side like a ship's canvas, with places in the centre for the arms."

Once the jury had reassembled, Verney Cave added that the failed crossbar was made of lancewood. He stressed Pilcher's faith in the Hawk, stating that Percy had "thought of building another like it." Ella had told him, he said, that "the cross-bar had been tested, and had borne both deceased and herself" before being placed in the machine.

Next to testify was Stanford Hall engineer John Hill, who said that he was standing in front of the machine when it "collapsed without any warning whatever." He thought that the accident was caused by the crossbar giving way, thereby allowing both wings to close up. He believed that the failure of the rudder line had put more weight on the crossbar, and that Pilcher had "jerked himself up in such a way as to bring yet further weight on to the cross-bar, and this might have caused it to snap."

Hill said that the wind was favorable for the trial, and pointed out that Pilcher had been very careful in his preparations, and overhauled his glider personally every time he used it.

Dr. Nash described the events after the crash and then Lord Braye, who was not sworn, made a statement, stressing Percy's desire that Henniker Heaton see the Hawk flying. The foreman asked if it was to be inferred that "because Mr. Henniker Heaton came down an attempt was made that otherwise would not have been made." Lord Braye would not go so far as to confirm that. He stated that he was at first led to believe that the "ascent" would not take place, but that as Pilcher was "satisfied that no additional danger would be caused by the weather no further opposition was made to it."

In summing up, the coroner said that the case

> need not give the jury very much trouble. Their duty was to ascertain what was the cause of death and whether there was any blame attached to anybody, or whether it was simply a pure accident. . . . They had probably seen statements in the papers that there was a certain amount of risk incurred in making a trial on Saturday on account of the weather; but that idea was set on one side by the evidence of Mr. Verney Cave and the engineer, who told them they considered the wind was not unfavourable to it. Outside people imagined there was more danger because there was a gale of wind, but really there was not that unnecessary risk being taken.

The coroner stated that it seemed to him that "all the jury could do was to return a verdict of accidental death." He said that such trials obviously entailed a certain amount of risk, but that "it was not for him to suggest that unnecessary risk was run, because he did not think there was. It was one of those unfortunate accidents which could not be prevented."

The jury concurred, and returned a verdict of "accidental death," expressing their regret that Pilcher "had lost his life in perfecting what, if he could have proved a success, would be some good to the world."

That evening Pilcher's body was conveyed by road to Rugby and then by rail to London. The funeral took place at Brompton Oratory, London, the next day, Wednesday, October 4, 1899. It was attended by "several engineering friends and workmen of the firm" as well as by the Honorable Verney Cave.[57] Pilcher was buried in grave number 162858 in Brompton Cemetery.[58] His tombstone bears the inscription: "In Loving Memory of PERCY SINCLAIR PILCHER who was killed whilst experimenting with his soaring machine at Stamford Hall, Yelvertoft. October 2nd 1899, Aged 32 years." The misspelling of Stanford Hall is curious.

Nowadays, investigations to determine the causes of aircraft accidents are invariably protracted affairs involving complex and detailed interpretations. However, those concerned have the advantage that their work begins immediately after the event, and they are often assisted by the impartial testimonies of "black box" recorders recovered from the wreckage and by the accounts of eyewitnesses.

Investigating a fatal accident that occurred nearly ninety years ago is more difficult. Only the latter of these sources of information are available, and they are by far the least reliable. Nonetheless, the fact that Pilcher's Hawk was a very simple structure greatly enhances the possibility of ascertaining the likely sequence of events that led to the disaster.

There are several eyewitness accounts of the crash, in the form of press reports or letters written shortly after the event by people closely concerned. All of these references are primary sources. There is no need or justification for recourse to secondary sources, which must (or should) depend upon the above for their information, and which may contain misleading assumptions.

Three principal questions must be answered:

1. Was the Hawk rain-soaked or not at the time of the accident, and, if it was, how might this have affected its performance?
2. Did Pilcher, who was normally a cautious and careful experimenter, take an unusual risk because he was anxious to impress Mr. Henniker Heaton?
3. What was the nature of the initial structural failure, and how did it cause the crash?

Percy Pilcher's grave in Brompton Cemetery as it appeared on April 9, 1983. (Author)

The first question is possibly the most important, as it is the key to the others. Unfortunately, we have contradictory contemporary statements. Engineer John Hill has already been quoted as saying: "The machine had been kept perfectly dry; and when the trial took place it was not raining." Baden-Powell, in the *Aeronautical Journal* for

October 1899, wrote: "The machine was then taken back for a fresh start, the inventor remarking that the rain had made the machine very heavy, and that it was difficult to get up the desired speed." An unnamed eyewitness (it could have been Baden-Powell again, of course) wrote in the *St. James's Gazette* for October 2: "The performer expressed his doubts whether his machine would soar well on account of the saturation of the canvas wings."

Who is correct? Baden-Powell and the anonymous writer are reporting *Pilcher's own statement* that the wings were wet and heavy, rather than making their own observations. For this reason the argument is in their favor. Hill, being several hundred yards away by the pulley system, would not have heard Percy's remarks. The fact that the towline broke twice before the fatal attempt also suggests that the glider was heavier than usual, for it is unlikely that Pilcher would have used a line of such marginal strength that it required constant repairs, thereby interrupting the trials. Such evidence tends to suggest that, although the glider had been under cover before the trials, it had become wet during the first attempts to take off.

The effects that this would have on the glider are obvious. It would increase its weight significantly—enough for Pilcher to notice its sluggishness, apparently—thereby raising its flying speed and increasing the stress borne by the structure. Moreover, the dampening of the fabric covering would cause it to shrink. As will be seen, the latter factor may have been critical.

The second question, that of unusual risk, is partly answered by the facts above. Pilcher was finding it "difficult to get up the desired speed" and the towline had parted twice, yet he persisted in his efforts to fly. As stated earlier, Lord Braye stressed at the inquest that Percy "was particularly anxious" that the trial should take place, "as Mr. Henniker Heaton, M.P., who had been interested in the invention, was amongst those present."[59] We also know that Henniker Heaton had been sent a copy of the prospectus of the syndicate "a few days before his [Pilcher's] death," for he states as much and quotes from it in a letter to the *Daily Graphic,* published on Saturday, October 7, 1899. He adds: "Aeronautics had always been a labour of love with him, entailing considerable drain both on his time and his pocket, and he had of late been trying to induce, with considerable success, one or two well-known engineers and scientific men to co-operate with him in raising funds for carrying on his experiments."

From the foregoing it is evident that there was sufficient motive to cause Pilcher to take unusual risk—unusual not in the sense that he made a wild misjudgment, but in the sense that, in his "anxiety" to draw another backer into the syndicate, he pushed his luck just a fraction too far. It could well be that his determination to impress overruled his caution.

The third question, that of ultimate cause and effect, is more complicated. Before analyzing the various statements, it is best to quote a few letters. On October 4, unaware of Percy's fatal accident, Lawrence Hargrave had written to Pilcher from 44 Rosslyn Gardens, Sydney, New South Wales:

> My dear Pilcher, At last there is a prospect of my doing a little more aeronautical work. My quarters here are the most roomy I have yet occupied, there are no facilities for soaring experiments but there is plenty of work to do with an oil motor or steam engine for the apparatus described in my paper on "Aeronautics." I think I can also improve the cellular kites, which, as you know, form the lifting surface. With kind regards to Wilson, believe me to be; Yours truly, Law. Hargrave.[60]

Only two days later Baden-Powell wrote to Hargrave:

> Dear Mr. Hargrave, I know you will be interested to know details about the sad accident to poor Pilcher. I was present at the experiment. He made some flights with great success in the machine very similar to that of Lilienthal, but drawn along the flat ground by a string—this gave it the requisite speed—and the balance of his body or rather his legs, caused it to ascend as required. On this occasion he went up beautifully & was perhaps 30 to 40 feet up when something went—it is difficult to say what—but I think the tail unit went first—then he lost his balance & struggled to regain it, but finally came down a crash to earth—both his legs were broken—we lifted him clear of the machine & carried him to the house. Where he [lingered or stayed] unconscious for 2 days & then quietly departed this life—He was a splendid workman—so energetic & so practical—it is a great loss to the cause of aeronautics.
>
> We had been trying the kites which you were so kind as to give us—just before the experiment. You will see a fuller account of the sad business in the Aeronautical Journal, which will I hope be out in a few days. Yours truly. B. Baden-Powell.

P.S. I have not got your address in Australia right—I hope you will get this soon.[61]

Also on October 6, Baden-Powell wrote to Chanute:

Dear Sir,

I know that you will be interested to know all about poor Pilcher. I was present when the accident occurred; but still am not able to give any very satisfactory evidence. The thing occurred so suddenly & it was so quickly over, & so much to occupy one's thoughts in trying to help the poor fellow immediately after, that I really cannot say quite what happened. He was well up—I judge about 30 or 40 ft.—when there was a crack—I think the tail seemed to collapse—the whole machine rocked greatly, probably through Pilcher trying hard to regain his balance—& then shot over forward & I think turned completely over before it fell to the ground. But it all occurred so instantaneously that all I can say for certain is that something suddenly went wrong & the machine fell to the ground.

As for other details I have put as full an account as possible in the Aeronautical Journal which you will shortly see—It is a very bad business. He had a new 3 decked machine very like yours, which he intended to try afterwards—

I must say it struck me as very dangerous to go up to the height he did. I think it would be better, as far as possible, never to let such a machine rise about 6 or 8 ft. & when well practised at this it could be tried to a good height over water.

He certainly did go most beautifully—rising quite easily from the level ground after a run of only a few yards—perhaps 10 or 15—& a very thin string, attached to the beak [?] sufficed to give the requisite speed.

Yours truly
B. Baden-Powell.[62]

Hargrave received his letter in mid-November, and replied to Baden-Powell on the 15th of that month:

Dear Capt. Baden-Powell, I had heard a rumour last week that someone was killed when trying a flying machine but your letter of Oct. 6 saying it was Pilcher is very distressing; let us hope that this is the last of those unstable single plane things that will be tried: I am doubtful when this will reach you as I think I saw your regiment had left for Africa: That is your brother I believe, that holds Mafeking. I hope he will soon assume the aggressive. Yours truly Law. Hargrave.[63]

Baden-Powell's account of the accident, published in the October issue of the *Aeronautical Journal,* was very brief, and very similar in content to his letter to Chanute.

Reports by those who examined the wreckage of the Hawk immediately after the accident attribute the mishap to two different initial failures, both connected with the tail.

The eyewitness writing in the *St. James's Gazette* of October 2 stated: "The apparent cause of the aeronaut's fall was the sudden fracture, while aloft, of a bamboo stick which 'spread' the 'tail,' on which the machine depends for balance. The saturation of the canvas caused the webbing to contract, until the slight bamboo spreader could no longer sustain the strain upon it." Baden-Powell offered the same explanation in the *Aeronautical Journal.* Laurence W. Miller, one of Pilcher's assistants who was present, adhered to this explanation when writing in *Flight* on March 5, 1910: "The cause of his fatal fall was due to the snapping of one of the bamboos supporting the tail-piece, or rudder."

The alternative cause was that offered by the Honorable Adrian Verney Cave and John Hill at the inquest. Reporting Verney Cave's evidence, the *Rugby Advertiser* stated: "Something seemed to go wrong with the rudder, and witness saw the cross-bar of the machine snap, whereupon the wings collapsed, and the machine came to the ground. In witness's opinion the cause of the collapse was the snapping of the cross-bar." It added, "since the accident witness had examined the machine, but he could not tell what caused the rudder to go. There were two lines fastening the rudder to the masts of the machine, and, in witness's opinion, one of these lines gave way."

John Hill was reported as saying that, in his opinion, "the cause of the accident was that the cross-bar gave way, causing the wings to close up. Previous to this, however, the rudder line had broken, throwing more weight on the cross-bar. Deceased jerked himself up in such a way as to bring yet further weight on to the cross-bar, and this might have caused it to snap." The *Leicester Daily Post* report added Hill's remark that "he did not think the deceased had ever contemplated the rudder lines breaking. They were of hemp, and about 1-16 of an inch thick." On this tack, the Honorable Everard Feilding wrote in a letter to the *Spectator,* published in the October 14 issue, that examination of the machine after the accident seemed to indicate that this was due . . . probably to the untying of a knot attaching the rudder to the machine. This itself was of small consequence, but necessitated a sudden movement on the part of the occupant to re-establish the equilibrium of the machine, thus bringing an unwonted strain on a certain spar, which parted and occasioned the collapse.

First, it must be made clear that the references to the "rudder" have to do with the fixed horizontal surface—what would now be called the tailplane. There were, indeed, two lines to this from the main kingposts, but there were also two more to the top of the fin. Whether the breakage or "untying" of one line would have been sufficient to cause the failure of the tailplane is difficult to say. However, it may have contributed to the snapping of one of the bamboo spreaders of the tail, which was already under stress owing to the shrinkage of the tailplane fabric.

The most significant points are that the glider "turned a complete somersault" (*Liverpool Post,* October 3) and Baden-Powell's emphatic underlining of the fact that it "shot over forward," in his letter to Chanute. These words point positively to a loss of download on the tailplane, which was set at a steep negative angle to keep the Hawk's nose up and to provide longitudinal stability. The failure of the bamboo spreader would have caused a marked loss of download on the tail, and no adjustment that Pilcher could have made by shifting his weight back would have been sufficient to compensate for it. The inevitable result would be for the glider to "somersault"—to turn over forward.

Pilcher's instinctive reaction, however, would have been to throw his weight back rapidly, and this movement, acting against the turning moment of the glider, would impose a torsional stress on the main beam between the wing kingposts, the Hawk's prime structural member. Baden-Powell's reference, in his letter to Chanute, to the fact that "the whole machine rocked greatly, probably through Pilcher trying to regain his balance," lends strength to this argument. Obviously, the breaking of this beam would result in the wings folding upward, as witnessed by Verney Cave and Hill. While these two witnesses were in the best position to see the wings fold—working the tow in front of the glider—they were in the worst possible position to see any failure in the tail, which would have been obscured by the wings.

Additional evidence of the main beam's failure was provided by T. W. K. Clarke, who restored the Hawk for the ASGB: "the member which broke with such disastrous results was the main transverse spar between the wing standards.''[64] Even shortly after the accident, the wreckage must have been such a mass of tangled wires, broken bamboo, and torn fabric that a broken tailplane spreader would have seemed of little significance compared with the failed beam. It is no surprise, therefore, that Clarke's attention fell wholly on the latter member eleven years later.

One other suggested explanation must be set aside. *Engineering,* in its issue for October 6, 1899, said:

> What really occurred is supposed to be that, desiring to descend, Mr. Pilcher shifted himself forward to depress the fore edge of the aeroplanes [wings], and a greater surface of the tail was thus suddenly exposed more directly to the force of the air. The soarer being still under propulsion, the increased pressure on the tail broke the tail guy cords, and there being now no force to elevate the fore end, which supported the weight of the man, it suddenly pointed earthward and fell without resistance through about 30 ft.

The basic fault in this reasoning is the assumption that Pilcher would decide to descend while still under tow. Descent was achieved by shifting the weight backward and without traction.

As we know that the glider turned over forward and fell on top of Pilcher, another question arises. If the Hawk hit the ground upside down why did Pilcher suffer fractures to both legs, rather than sustaining injuries to the upper half of his body? A study of the glider's somersault and the way in which its pilot may have been thrown about offers a possible and plausible explanation. As the glider nosed over, Pilcher may well have been pitched upward through the oval ''fuselage'' frame. It seems reasonable to assume that he would have been grasping the pegs firmly in his attempts to right the machine. As the glider became inverted, Pilcher's hips and legs could have fallen through the fuselage frame, his body rotating around his shoulders until he was beneath the falling structure, his legs lowest and facing the tail of the glider, which itself was now pointing in what had been the direction of flight. In this position his legs would have hit the ground first, sustaining severe fractures, and the glider would have fallen inverted on top of him, as reported. The accompanying diagram illustrates the suggested sequence.

Pilcher's death certificate, dated December 6, 1899, reveals that he died intestate. The gross value of his estate was given as £150 8s 6d,

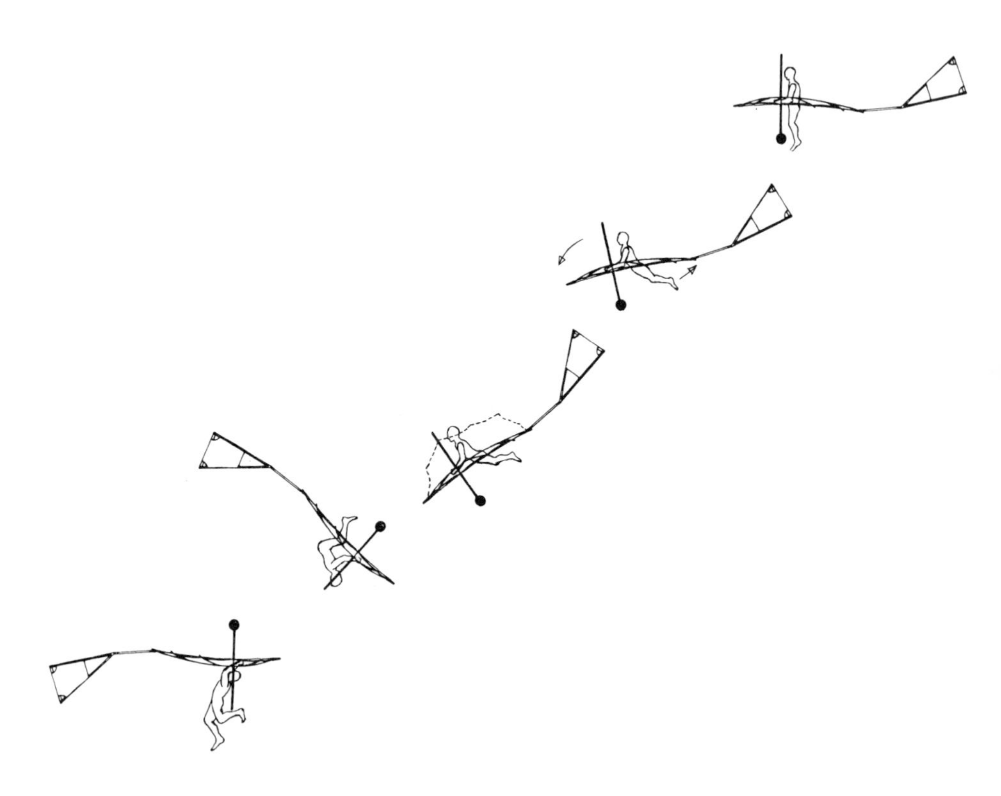

This sequential diagram illustrates the way in which Pilcher could have been thrown about in his glider in the fatal accident of September 30, 1899. No attempt has been made to show the movements of the damaged tail or the folding of the wings, of which sufficient detail is lacking. From top to bottom: the glider is flying level under tow; the breaking of the tailplane spreader causes loss of download and the Hawk begins to turn over forward—Pilcher throws his weight back; the wing main beam fails under stress and the wings begin to fold upward, the glider continues to somersault; as the glider turns over, the pilot's hips and legs fall through the body frame, aided by the turning moment; the glider upside down just before impact. Pilcher has fallen through the frame and faces the tail, with the glider above him. His legs will hit the ground first.

and the net value of his personal estate was £39 19s 0d. Pilcher's estate was left to Ada Violet Gallier Robinson of 14 Lexham Gardens, Gloucester Road, London, the wife of George Thomas Robinson and Percy's natural and lawful sister.[65]

Many newspapers published reports of the tragic accident and tributes to the dead pioneer. Some of these tributes came from those who had known him or worked alongside him in a common cause: the conquest of air. When interviewed by the *Daily Mail,* Maxim stated: "It was Pilcher's intention, when he had succeeded in balancing himself in the air, to apply a motor to the machine and do away with the cord." He continued, "My own experiments have proved that propulsion and lifting power may be obtained by mechanical means, and the experiments of Lilienthal and Pilcher show that sometimes one can balance himself in the air."[66] In the *Leicester Daily Post* for October 4 he was reported as saying, in part "Mr. Pilcher had one thing that I can't get. He had no motive or lifting power, but he had a balance. Now, I made a machine self-propelling, and with a lifting power of 10,000 lb., besides its own weight. But I never dared trust myself to it, because I could not manage the balance. That is the crux of the question."[67]

A correspondent writing as "one who knew him" in the *Daily Graphic* for October 7, 1899, after quoting documents sent to him by Henniker Heaton, concludes by saying "He did a good deal to advance the solution of the problem of balancing in the air, and the science has lost in him a student modest, manly, and sincere."

One signing himself "E.F."—presumably the Honorable Everard Feilding—wrote in the *Spectator* of October 14:

> While hesitating to encourage others to engage in a problem of which past history is so stained with tragedy, one cannot but deplore the possibility of Mr. Pilcher's results dying with himself. Many of his notes are in existence, together with the drawings of his apparatus and a new and hitherto untried machine. It is to be hoped that these may prove of service to other and more fortunate investigators.

It is clear from Pilcher's own remarks that his ultimate aim was powered, heavier-than-air flight. His gliders were merely "first primers" toward this goal, as evidenced by the statement in his January 1897 lecture to the Military Society of Ireland:

> The object of experimenting with soaring machines is to enable one to have practice in starting and alighting and controlling a machine in the air. They cannot possibly float horizontally in the air for any length of time, but to keep going must necessarily lose in elevation. They are excellent schooling machines, and that is all they are meant to be, until power, in the shape of an engine working a screw propeller, or an engine working wings to drive the machine forward, is added, then a person who is used to sailing down a hill with a simple soaring machine

will be able to fly with comparative safety. One can best compare them to bicycles having no cranks, but on which one could learn to balance by coming down an incline.[68]

Whether Pilcher considered his weight-shift control adequate is uncertain, but he was acutely aware that it severely restricted the size of his gliders and presented even greater problems when the weight of an engine was added. He was also aware of Chanute's dissatisfaction with this aspect, and there is every likelihood that, if he had made "marginally powered" flights in his triplane, he would have used the vital extra time in the air to explore alternative control systems.

Following its report of the inquest, the *Rugby Advertiser* of October 7 wrote: "Had Mr. Pilcher succeeded in controlling and propelling the machine, which he was confident of doing, he would have accomplished one of the greatest inventions of his life. He fully recognised that the first step to be attained was the power to balance himself in the air and in this he had succeeded." The important point about this statement is that it differentiates, quite clearly, between "balance" (stability) and "control." The introductory piece to the same article noted that "his main object at present was to overcome the difficulties of controlling and steering such machines when in mid-air."

With the longer flights made possible by the addition of a small engine, perhaps Pilcher would have been able to devise a control system using auxiliary surfaces rather than body-swinging. In 1923 Pilcher's partner, Walter Wilson, said, "He was considering rudder control, and would have experimented with this had he lived, and of course Aileron control was unknown to him."[69] Wilbur Wright revealed his realization of the vital need for longer flying times in his oft-quoted first letter to Octave Chanute on May 13, 1900. Describing a tower and pulley system that he envisaged as a means of making tethered tests of a tentative manned "apparatus," he wrote:

> If the plan will only enable me to remain in the air for practice by the hour instead of by the second, I hope to acquire the skill sufficient to overcome both these difficulties [i.e., those imposed by the system itself] and those inherent to flight. Knowledge and skill in handling the machine are absolute essentials to flight and it is impossible to obtain them without extensive practice. The method employed by Mr. Pilcher of towing with horses in many respects is better than that I propose to

employ, but offers no guarantee that the experimenter will escape accident long enough to acquire skill sufficient to prevent accident.

Shortly after comes the now famous remark: "My observation of the flight of buzzards leads me to believe that they regain their lateral balance, when partly overturned by a gust of wind, by a torsion of the tips of the wings."[70]

Hindsight enables us to see that Pilcher's decision to apply power before fully mastering control and the Wrights' mastery of control before the application of power were, respectively, the routes to failure and to ultimate success. Once a control system independent of pilot weight was devised, wing area could be increased as necessary to lift a motor of the required power. Pilcher may well have encountered formidable control problems in a powered hang glider.

The question of whether the powered Hawk or triplane would have been capable of sustained flight is intriguing. Detailed calculations for the powered Hawk in an undated document probably prepared in the 1930s[71] assume an all-up weight of 300 pounds with engine, propeller, tanks, and fuel. Rather strangely, the document first concludes that, with a 4½-horsepower engine, there was an excess of power of ½ horsepower allowing a rate of climb of 45 feet per minute at the 26.26 miles per hour estimated takeoff speed, but that all available power would be absorbed in flying at the maximum speed of only 30 miles per hour. The margin was very small. Following a statement that the Hawk "would have flown provided that the weight all up could have been kept down to 300 lbs.," the report destroys this claim by adding that the 4½ horsepower would have to be the power delivered at the propeller, and concludes: "Owing to the fact that a propeller is working on air, a fluid medium, there is a loss of about 25% in propeller slip, thus the engine would need to be able to develop 25% more than 4½ h.p. that is 5.625, but say 5.75 or 5¾ h.p."

Pilcher planned for only 4 horsepower, and the anonymous mathematician who produced eleven pages of calculations to reach these contradictory conclusions makes no allowance for the fact that early propellers were far from efficient. (Pilcher would have used a wide-chord "fan"-type two-blader like those used by Maxim.) So it seems that the powered Hawk, even with a headwind, was a very marginal proposition.

The same is true of the 4-horsepower powered triplane, according to figures worked out by Mike Hirst from the bare details provided by the author. Two drag equations were produced, one based upon the best drag coefficients for the various components of the aircraft, the other based upon "assumed worst" figures. His conclusions were as follows: "Plots of power requirements show that minimum power speed would have been around 30 m.p.h., and that to maintain straight and level flight would have required about 2.8 to 3.0 h.p. at the propeller. This suggests that an overall propeller efficiency of 70% to 75% was needed."

The calculations showed that the aircraft would have stalled at about 25 miles per hour and cruised at only 5 miles per hour above this speed. Mike Hirst stated:

> The drag calculations suggest that minimum drag would have been between 31–35 lb. (at 35 m.p.h.), compared with the 30lb. drag (at 25 m.p.h.) that he [Pilcher] measured on the Hawk glider. The triplane, without engine, would have flown faster than the Hawk, but [would] have been more efficient. Using Hawk figures again, dropping 5 ft./sec. at 25 m.p.h. suggests that he had demonstrated an L/D [lift/drag ratio] of about 7.3, whereas my calculations suggest that even with an engine the triplane would have achieved an L/D between 7.5 and 8.6.[72]

Commenting on these figures, John Bagley of the Science Museum stated that he "had no trouble doubling Mike Hirst's drag estimates." He believed that the triplane's wing cutouts would have markedly increased the induced drag.[73]

However, all of these calculations are again settled by the question of propeller efficiency. Pilcher would never have even approached the minimum 70 percent efficiency required by Mike Hirst's reckoning. The first to do so were the Wright Brothers, who achieved some 66 percent in 1903, after extensive original research and calculation. It is unlikely that 50–55 percent was exceeded before that.

The sad conclusion, therefore, is that the powered triplane would probably have been incapable of sustained horizontal flight, though it would have made a better glider than the Hawk. Like Herring in the United States, Pilcher had followed a path that led, at the time, into a blind alley. Even if he had made tentative powered hops, without an adequate control system the whole problem was greatly compounded by the conflicting demands of weight, wing area, and manageability.

Many aeronautical writers and journalists have stated categorically that, had Pilcher lived, he might well have achieved successful powered flight before the Wright Brothers. This is a purely speculative claim that cannot be supported by evidence. In fact, Pilcher made no revolutionary scientific or technical contributions to the advancement of aeronautics, and his work always followed in the footsteps of others. Wilbur Wright estimated that Lilienthal had amassed only some five hours in the air in five years of gliding.[74] There is no means of reckoning Pilcher's total flying time for 1895–99, but it was certainly much less than even that small total.

Nonetheless, Pilcher did make a contribution to the final achievement of powered flight. At the conclusion of the First Pilcher Memo-

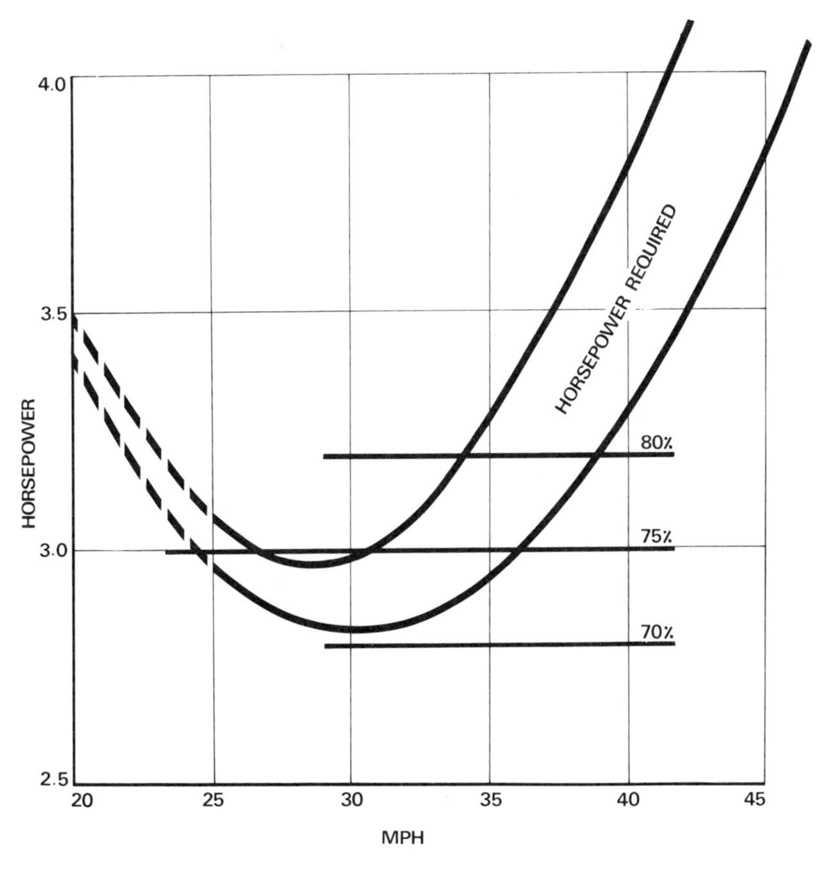

Mike Hirst's estimated performance curves for the powered triplane.

rial Lecture, delivered before the Glasgow Branch of the Royal Aeronautical Society on February 10, 1956, Ian R. Liddell said:

> His persistence in pursuing the line which he had chosen was of much greater value in what it failed to achieve, than in what it achieved, for it was largely by studying the results of the experiments of Lilienthal, Pilcher, Chanute and Langley that the Wright Brothers were confirmed in the initial direction of their own experiments. Wilbur said that there did not appear in fact to be any flying art in the proper sense of the word but only a flying problem. The Wrights therefore started by avoiding the things which the work of others had demonstrated to be hindrances rather than contributory to a solution of the problem.[75]

In a paper read before the Western Society of Engineers on September 18, 1901, Wilbur Wright said:

> Although the fatalities which befell the designers of [the Lilienthal and Pilcher] machines were due to the lack of structural strength, rather than to lack of control, nevertheless it had become clear to the students of the problem that a more perfect method of control must be evolved.[76]

In helping to put this vital message across, Percy Sinclair Pilcher gave his life. He was the first man in Britain to design, construct, and make successful flights in heavier-than-air aircraft, and he was the first man in Britain—and only the second in the world after Lilienthal—to die in an accident to a conventional fixed-wing airplane. Sadly, there was no one in Britain to continue his work, and the lead passed to America—the very thing that Percy hoped would not happen. It was on the new continent and in the new century that the great conquest was made, but it was the devotion and sacrifice of Pilcher and his kind that blazed the trail.

Postscript

The Fate of the Surviving Original Gliders

At a Council meeting of the Aeronautical Society of Great Britain on December 5, 1899, Percy's sister Ella was elected an Honorary Member of the society, and the council passed a resolution "recording their sense of the valuable services contributed by the late Mr. Pilcher to the subject of aeronautics, and feel the great loss which the Society has sustained by his untimely death in carrying out his practical aerial experiment." It added: "The Council also desires to express their deep sympathy with Miss Pilcher, an Honorary Member of the Society, in her irreplaceable loss."[1]

On October 21 a deputation from the ASGB had attended Chelsea Barracks to wish Major Baden-Powell "a hearty farewell, and a safe and speedy return," for his regiment, the Scots Guards, was departing for South Africa and the Boer War. Baden-Powell was therefore unable to attend the above meeting, but we can be sure that he would have endorsed the resolution.

An announcement in the January 1900 issue of the *Aeronautical Journal* stated that, because of the "widespread interest" in Pilcher's work, the society had arranged with the management of the Crystal Palace that his flying machines would go on exhibition there.[2]

By the next issue, that for April, this had been accomplished, and an advertisement announced: "Crystal Palace, Sydenham. The Pilcher Collection of Soaring machines, including the machine on which the late Mr. PERCY PILCHER met with his fatal accident, are now on view by arrangement with the Aeronautical Society of Great Britain."[3]

A report in the same issue[4] stated that Pilcher's gliders had been presented to the ASGB by the Wilson and Pilcher firm, "and form a substantial addition to the Museum, which it is Major Baden-Powell's wish to develop in connection with the Society." After announcing the Crystal Palace exhibition, the article listed and described the machines thus:

> 1. Lilienthal's Soaring Machine. With this type of machine, Herr Lilienthal met with his fatal accident. [This was, of course, the No. 11 glider that Dr. Bennett had given to Pilcher. There is no record of it ever being flown by either Bennett or Pilcher.]
> 2. Pilcher's Soaring Machine, with which he met with his recent fatal accident. . . . This machine is exhibited in the damaged condition it was found in after it was precipitated to the earth with the unfortunate experimenter.
> 3. Pilcher's new and incompleted soaring machine. This is constructed on the principle of the Hargrave soaring kite, and consists of a large number of small wings placed in sets one above the other, and it was upon this machine that the oil engine, made by Messrs. Pilcher, was intended to be placed.

The last paragraph was to lead to statements in subsequent accounts that the triplane owed its origins to the Hargrave soaring kite, a much-repeated mistruth, which led to the "disappearance" of the important Pilcher-Chanute link until it was rediscovered by the present writer in 1972. The reference to "Messrs. Pilcher" as builders of the engine is obviously a misprint of "Messrs. Wilson and Pilcher."

Because of their fragile construction the gliders began to deteriorate within a short time, and at an ASGB Council meeting on September 25, 1900, they were reported to be "in a very dilapidated condition." It was left to the discretion of Eric Stuart Bruce, the society's honorary secretary, "either to find some member of the Society who would house them free of expense, or if no one could be found to put them into some scientific sale to save further expense to the Society."[5]

Fortunately, the latter proposal was avoided. At a council meeting on January 31, 1901, it was stated that the relics were now in the care of member E. P. Frost, who had agreed to house them "for the present" on the society's behalf.[6] This arrangement had been suggested by Hiram Maxim in a letter to Bruce dated September 27, 1900.[7] The gliders remained in Frost's care until 1906. At a council meeting on December 7 that year the honorary secretary announced that Frost could no longer store them, and stated that he (the honorary secretary) had arranged with the Alexandra Palace authorities that they should go on exhibition there.[8] Although they were at the Alexandra Palace by April 1907, they were not unpacked. The society's honorary secretary wanted the gliders to be hung on view, but it was uncertain whether they were in a "sufficiently presentable state to be exhibited."[9]

No more is heard of the gliders until 1909, when the Hawk and the Lilienthal machine were displayed on the society's stand at the Travel, Sports and Pastimes Exhibition at Olympia, which opened on July 6. In preparation for this exhibition, the ASGB had both gliders repaired by Messrs. T. W. K. Clarke, a leading glider manufacturer. *Flight* reported that "the work has been carried out with great fidelity to the most authentic records which exist, so that the two gliders as they stand to-day may be taken as being absolutely what the intrepid but unlucky pioneers used in their experiments."[10] Clarke, it was reported, had done "a considerable amount of careful work" to restore them to a presentable state. An offshoot of this work was a two-part feature in *Flight,* probably written by Clarke.[11] It will be noticed that the triplane has already started to fade away.

In August 1909 the Hawk was loaned to the Royal Scottish Museum (now the Royal Museum of Scotland), Edinburgh, and put on display.[12] It remained there until some time after March 18, 1911, when it was borrowed from the museum, with the ASGB's consent, by the Scottish Aeronautical Society for display at the Glasgow Exhibition, the Scottish Aeronautical Society having undertaken to insure it against fire loss or damage.[13] On Sunday November 5, 1911, the aviation building in which the Hawk was housed was wrecked by a storm and the glider was "very badly damaged." It was then discovered that the Scottish Aeronautical Society had not insured against loss or damage, but only against fire and lightning, and its honorary secretary wrote disclaiming all liability. The remains of the Hawk were returned to the Royal Scottish Museum, which offered to repair the glider free of charge.

By late January 1912 the museum was able to report that the Hawk was repaired and restored. Regrettably, it seems that the fabric was attached to the underside of the wing in error, and this mistake, along with others, has been faithfully adhered to in subsequent restorations and in all but one of the reproductions built (see appendix E).

The next recorded appearance was in a temporary "Exhibition of apparatus illustrating the application of scientific principles to Aeronautics," which was set up in the Science Museum, South Kensington, from December 23, 1912, until the end of January 1913.[14] It then appeared on the ASGB's stand at the Fourth International Aero Show at Olympia, London, during February 14–22, 1913.[15] Royal Museum of Scotland (RMS) records show that the Hawk was "Returned from Olympia" on March 3, but the *Aeronautical Journal* for April 1913 reports that, by arrangement with the Board of Trade, the society had lent the Hawk for display in the British Section of the Ghent International Exhibition. It was returned to the RSM on January 16, 1914.[16]

On March 24, 1920, the Hawk was given to the RSM on a permanent basis. At this time it was on display in the Machinery Hall, where it remained until 1939. Upon the outbreak of the Second World War, the Hawk was taken down to be put into storage, whereupon it was found that its fabric wing covering had rotted. The glider remained in store until March 17, 1961, when it was transported to Old Warden Aerodrome, Bedfordshire, for restoration, with the Royal Aeronautical Society's consent, by the Shuttleworth Trust under the watchful eye of manager Sqn. Ldr. L. A. Jackson. By March 1962 Jackson was able to write to Lord Braye that "the restoration of the Pilcher is going very well and I am now doing the wing covers, having licked the frame and tail into shape."[17] The new fabric was to be carefully copied from the old remnants. The work was completed in 1963, and the glider was returned to the RMS on November 12 and placed on display once more. It has been allotted the British Aicraft Preservation Council No. BAPC 49.

Strange to relate, another of Pilcher's gliders survived into the 1920s, but it is now impossible to determine which one it was. Writing in 1934,[18] Sam Mavor said: "It is much to be regretted that the most successful of the gliders made by Pilcher while in Glasgow has not been preserved [this discounts the Hawk, which was built, but not flown, in Scotland]. The historic relic was in possession of the University, and through some carelessness or misunderstanding, it was destroyed." This undoubtedly alludes to the Bat, and in a letter to Ella dated January 21, 1937, another Pilcher researcher, Robert C. Gray, Glasgow University's lecturer in applied physics, wrote: "One machine was left at Glasgow University, probably the 'Bat.' I have spent much time trying to find this glider; it was at the University in 1923, but I cannot trace what happened to it."[19]

The Hawk after its early 1960s restoration on display in the Royal Museum of Scotland, where it is still to be seen. (Rolls-Royce)

Gray contradicted himself eighteen years later when he wrote, "One of his three Scottish gliders, probably the 'Beetle' was left by him at the University when he left in 1896; it was finally broken up in 1923."[20] Whether Mr. Gray had unearthed more information, or whether his memory was simply at fault, we may never know.

The fate of the triplane is also mysterious. We know from the report in the April 1900 *Aeronautical Journal* that it was intact at that time. By December 20, 1910, when T. W. K. Clarke made drawings of triplane components, it had obviously been broken down, and only two half-wings (i.e., two two-panel units) and one separate panel survived.[21] These fragments—or some of them, at least—were offered to the Science Museum in 1928 by the Council of the RAeS, "with a view to their reconstruction for exhibition in the National Aeronautical Collection." In fact, the Science Museum concluded that the components offered constituted "parts of two different gliders," comprising "an incomplete wing of a biplane or triplane glider and . . . the covering of a monoplane glider." Although the fragments were at the museum from April 27 to July 10, 1928, it was concluded that "there is not . . . sufficient material to reconstruct either of these gliders, as, in each case, the important timber structure is absent and there is insufficient data to reproduce it with confidence," and they were returned to the society.[22] The identity of the monoplane fabric is unknown. We next hear of the triplane in the aforementioned letter from Robert Gray to Ella in 1937, when he says: "The Royal Aeronautical Society in London have . . . bits of another machine that cannot be identified."[23]

Nothing was then heard of the triplane components until 1959, when they were shown on a BBC television program in a series entitled "Lost without Trace," broadcast on August 6, which centered on the missing engine. The program's presenter, Andrew Sinclair, said: "When we started work on the programme, the Royal Aeronautical Society told us they had a parcel of Pilcher relics which had been there unopened for many years. When we opened it we found in it these pieces of material which seem to be a wing of this triplane."[24] Even these few remaining traces of Pilcher's last glider have now vanished, but the author was fortunate to receive a letter from Mr. Ted Shreeve, in which he recalled their appearance (see chapter 5). In a letter written in June 1978, Mr. Shreeve wrote that he saw the relics when they were being shown to visiting BBC staff. He said:

> The relics, with a collection of 'Pilcher' photographs, which, I think, came originally from his sister, were brought to the end 'BLACK SHED,' on the railway straight, at Hendon Aerodrome. This was, at the time, the store and workshop for the RAeS Nash Collection of Historical Aircraft. The material was brought by Alec Lumsden—at the time employed by the RAeS—and was unwrapped in the centre of the hangar, between the aircraft.
>
> The relics arrived in a thin brown paper parcel—approx. 18″ × 12″ × 1″ to 1.5″, tied with string and with the word 'Pilcher' in ink or blue pencil on one side. When [it was] opened up, I spread the contents out to get some idea of the layout, and found three or four timber components, a fabric sail and several bits of thin string and tape joining these together.[25]

Mr. Shreeve's sketches—drawn from memory—are shown here. He also supplied a description of the components. From the foregoing it is obvious that the triplane has gradually "disintegrated" over the years. One day these last few pieces—presently lost—may resurface. It is devoutly hoped that they will be properly cared for if they do.

Other Pilcher memorabilia held in the RAeS library came from his sister Ella. At an ASGB Council meeting on March 11, 1902, the honorary secretary informed the meeting that Ella had offered to

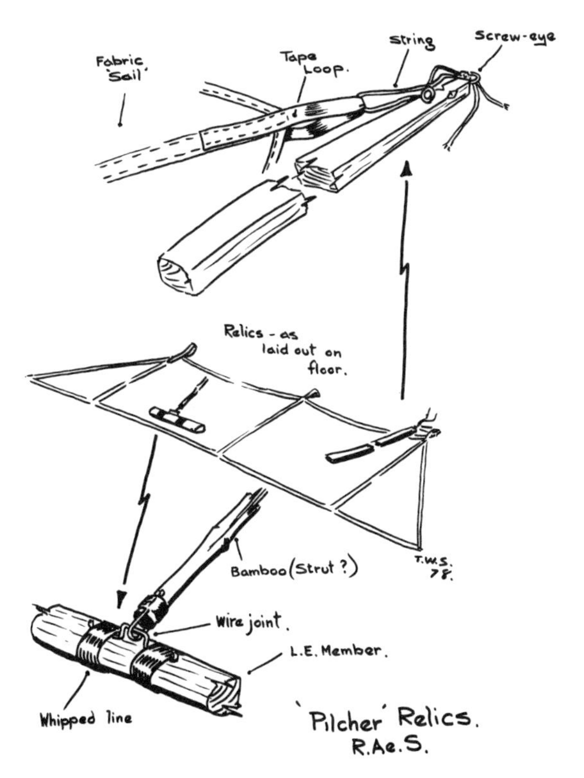

Mr. Ted Shreeve's 1978 drawings from memory of the surviving fragments of Pilcher's triplane, which he saw at Hendon Aerodrome in 1959.

present the society with "the collection of note books, books, lantern slides and photographs which had been the property of the late Mr. Percy Pilcher."

"Resolved," report the minutes, "that these valuable relics of the late Mr. Percy Pilcher be accepted and the best thanks of the Council conveyed to Miss Ella Pilcher for her generous present." The society's acquisition of this material was announced at a meeting at the Society of Arts on the same day.[26]

Ella also wrote a short account of her brother's work for the *Aeronautical Journal* under her married name, Tidswell.[27] Unfortunately it is full of vagaries and demonstrable errors. Even more unfortunately, many writers have accepted it as a reliable factual account simply because it is by Percy's sister, and many errors have been perpetuated as a result.

Appendix A

An Undated Engine

The Royal Aeronautical Society Library holds an additional engine drawing by Pilcher that cannot be fitted into the account because it is undated.

A full-scale, four-view sectioned engineering drawing, it depicts one cylinder casting for an upright, two-cylinder inline engine of unspecified type, with a bore of 2 inches and an overall height of 9$^{3}/_{16}$ inches. Using this drawing, technical artist Frank Munger prepared the perspective sketch reproduced here, showing the appearance of a complete cylinder casting and of the complete two-cylinder unit. The crankshaft is indicated by the broken line at the top.

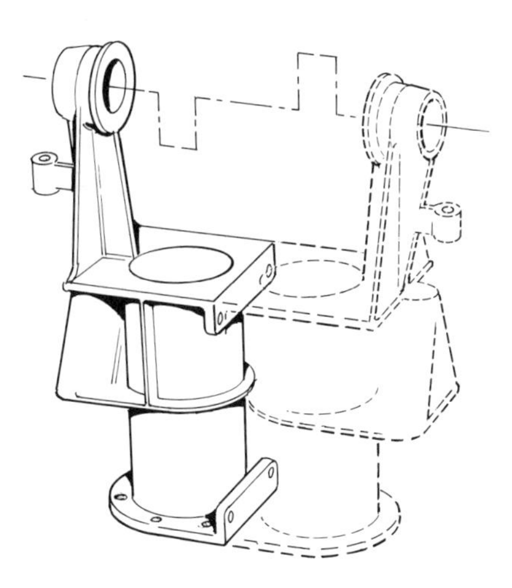

The functions of the small guide tubes extending from the crankshaft supports is obscure, as is the purpose of the bifurcated V-shaped tubes below them (but not in line with them), each of which measured 3/4 inches in inside diameter and was threaded internally.

The drawing contains no written information other than dimensions, but written across the bottom is "Cancelled in favour of 1 Cyl." This suggests that the drawing was made some years before the two-cylinder horizontally opposed petrol engine was built for the triplane, during 1898–99.

Appendix B

Patents

Ten patents were applied for either by Pilcher alone, or by Pilcher in association with Wilson. Of these, the three major ones to be granted—those for the glider, the Cyclone sail, and the furnace-gas and steam engine—are reproduced in the following pages by kind permission of the Controller of Her Majesty's Stationery Office. The complete list of patents applied for is as follows:

No.	*Date of application*	*Subject*	*Remarks*
20,767	November 2, 1893	Matchbox holder	See main text
20,768	November 2, 1893	Covers for glasses, cups, etc.	See main text
15,614	August 17, 1894	Signaling apparatus	Abandoned, see main text
21,024	November 2, 1894	Captive balloons, kites, etc.	Abandoned
9144	April 30, 1896	Improvements in flying and soaring machines	Accepted March 6, 1897; see this appendix and text
29,194	December 19, 1896 (with Wilson)	Improvements in sails for boats, etc.	Accepted December 11, 1897; see this appendix and text
11,619	May 10, 1897	Furnace-gas and steam engines	Accepted April 16, 1898; see this appendix and text
1100	January 17, 1899 (with Wilson)	Electric light brackets	Abandoned
3941	February 22, 1899 (with Wilson)	Wheels	Abandoned
10,589	May 19, 1899 (with Wilson)	Wheels	Abandoned

N° 9144  A.D. 1896

Date of Application, 30th Apr., 1896

Comp ete Specification Left, 22nd Jan.. 1897—Accepted, 6th Mar., 1897

PROVISIONAL SPECIFICATION.

Improvements in Flying and Soaring Machines.

I PERCY SINCLAIR PILCHER of Artillery Mansions Victoria Street London S.W. Gentleman, do hereby declare the nature of this invention to be as follows:—

The invention refers to improved soaring and flying machines which are 5 intended to carry one aeronaut, and particularly to the provisions made for keeping the wings rigid, and for enabling them to be folded up and to the means of supporting the aeronaut in the machine.

The soaring machine consists of two wings, a rudder and frame work for holding the above, two wheels with springs may be attached for the machine to run on 10 when on the ground, and for taking any jar there may be on alighting. The flying machine is similar to the soaring machine, but has an oil, spirit, or other engine attached to the frame-work and connected to drive one or two screw propellers working in the air placed preferably just above the front of the machine, or two screw-propellers one placed under each wing. The main frame consists of two 15 masts placed from about 6 to 10 ft. apart according to size of machine and each having a total height of about 6 to 8 ft. and standing vertical or approximately vertical when the wings are horizontal; these are connected to each other by an upper cross-bar at or near the top of the masts and again another cross-bar preferably curved down slightly in the middle at or near the centre of the masts. 20 There are also wires from the lower cross-bar to the bottom of the masts and to the upper cross-bar at or near its junctions to the masts.

There is a fore and aft body piece composed of two pieces of bamboo, wood or steel tube, connected together at the ends by being held in suitable castings or by other means.

25 The aeronaut takes up his position in the body piece the width of which is about 20 inches for an ordinary sized man but may be more or less according to his size, one of the bamboos passing on either side of him; to each of the bamboos there is a vertical handle attached, which the aeronaut holds in his hands, about a foot abaft which are two straps or tubes which are padded and through which his fore-30 arms pass so that when carrying the machine he takes the weight chiefly by means of the straps and is able to tilt it as he wishes by means of the handles; when he is resting on the machine his weight is taken on the padding under the straps, or on the body-piece, and holding tightly on to the handles he is able to move the weight of his body forwards and backwards so as to balance the machine in a fore 35 and aft direction when it is supported in the air.

This body piece rests on the lower cross-bar of the main frame and is held to it by lashings or by other means. From the ends of this body piece wires are attached the tops and bottoms of the masts and keep them from moving in a fore and aft direction. The wings are stiffened by means of a series of spokes radiating 40 from the mast just above the junction with the lower cross-piece. These spokes are made preferably of bamboo though other materials such as straight grained wood or steel tube may be substituted.

These spokes are stayed or braced by means of wires leading to the tops and bottoms of the masts or to some suitable connection made to the tops and bottoms 45 of the masts.

There are preferably two wires from the shorter of the spokes to the top

[P...

and two wires to the bottom of each mast but in the case of the longer spokes there are three wires to the top and three to the bottom of the mast from each spoke, but there may be more or less.

The connection of each spoke to the mast is made by having a metal piece rigidly attached to the spoke and passing completely round the mast but allowing 5 sufficient freedom for the spoke to be revolved round the mast. In each wing there are about 8 or 9 spokes which or some of which pass through pockets sewn on to the under side of the sails confining the sails to the spokes and keeping the spokes from bending sideways. The sail is attached to the end of each spoke by means of a lashing made between an eye in the end of the spoke and loops made of tape in 10 suitable positions on the sail, but this may be effected by other means.

As the spokes pass through the pockets under the sail the wires from the spokes to the tops of the masts must necessarily pass through the sail. In order that the wires shall not tear the sail where they pass through a hole 1 to 2 inches in diameter is cut through the sail for each wire. Round the edge of each of these holes is 15 glued a patch of sail cloth or other material, which is afterwards varnished over, so as to keep the wire from tearing the sail.

The sails are made of closely woven cotton or other similar material, but gold-beater's skin may be used.

The width over the wing tips of the whole machine is from about twenty to 20 thirty feet and the length fore and aft over wings from about seven to 12 feet. These sizes will vary with the weight of the aeronaut, the amount of wind, in the case of soaring machines; and the speed at which it is intended to drive in the case of flying machines having motive power.

The front of the body-piece extends a foot or so in front of the forward edge of 25 the wings, so that it will receive the blow in the event of the machine striking anything end on, and also to give the wires from the forward end of the body piece to the masts a better lead, as the main frame is in front of the centre of the body piece.

The sails are laced to the body piece; there is a division in each sail from the 30 mast to the body piece and to the inner edge of the sail in line with the main frame which is laced up when the sail is set. So that having all these details as described if these lacings are cast off the whole of the spokes and sails are free to revolve round the mast and thus the wings are furled.

The wings are slightly curved both fore and aft and transversely, concave on the 35 lower side. The fore and aft curvature is given because at small angles to the wind the lifting power is greater for the same resistance to forward motion, and the longitudinal balance can be easily controlled because the longitudinal shift of the centre of lift is less in the case of a suitably curved surface than of a plain.

The transverse curvature of the sails is such that the body piece is lowest; each 40 sail rises towards its centre and drops again towards its tip, the tip being preferably about 6 inches or a foot above the body piece.

The rudder has preferably transverse surface only but it may have vertical surface also; the transverse surface is slightly inclined to the wing surface, being raised at the after edge. 45

The surface of the transverse rudder is about one tenth of the area of the surface of the wing that is to say if the wing area is 170 sq. ft. the transverse rudder surface will be about 17 sq. ft., this may be modified in particular machines in order to counteract a bad distribution of the weight in a fore and aft direction.

The rudder is attached to the after end of the body piece and is connected in 50 such a way that it may be raised but it can not be depressed relatively to the wings so that on alighting if the rudder be struck it will simply lift and take no shock and in the air it will enable the aeronaut by throwing his weight back on the machine to throw the machine up in front more quickly than would be the case if the rudder were not free to lift; but as the rudder cannot be depressed the 55 transverse surface will keep the machine from taking a sudden pitch forward.

The rudder is kept from moving sideways by means of lines going to the extremities of the spokes in the after sides of the sails and from depressing by lines attached to the tops of the masts on the upper cross-piece.

The wheels are attached by means of suitable arrangements to the bottoms of the masts and the lower cross-bar, this latter connection containing a spring, and their 5 motion in a fore and aft direction is constrained by wires to the end of the body piece.

Dated this 30th day of April 1896.

PERCY SINCLAIR PILCHER.

COMPLETE SPECIFICATION.

10 **Improvements in Flying and Soaring Machines.**

I, Percy Sinclair Pilcher of Artillery Mansions, Victoria Street, London S.W. Gentleman do hereby declare the nature of this invention and in what manner the same is to be performed, to be particularly described and ascertained in and by the following statement:—

15 This invention refers to improved soaring and flying machines which are intended to carry an aëronaut, and it refers particularly to the means for keeping the wings rigid and for enabling them to be folded up, and to the means for supporting the aëronaut in or on the said machines.

20 Fig. 1 of the accompanying drawings represents a soaring machine in longitudinal elevation constructed according to my invention.

Fig. 2 is a similar view, with the wings removed, of a flying machine which is constructed practically in the same manner as a soaring machine except that it is provided with means for propelling.

25 Fig. 3 is a part front or end elevation of same and

Fig. 4 is a plan.

The soaring machine consists of two wings A made of light fabric or the like a rudder or tail B and a frame work for holding same. Two wheels 3 mounted freely on shafts 2 may be attached to the machine to run on the ground, and for 30 neutralizing to a great extent any jar there may be on alighting the inner ends of the shafts 2 are pivoted to the bottoms S^1 of the masts, and the other ends of the shafts are connected by a rod 4 to a tube 5 containing a helical spring not shown. The lines or wires 1 serve to limit the outward motion of the rods 4 in the tubes 5 and also to limit the movement of the wheels in a fore and aft direction. The 35 flying machine is similar to the soaring machine, but has an oil, spirit, or other engine U attached to the framework preferably just above the machine and connected to drive a screw propeller W working in the air. Or the engine may be behind and the propeller in front or there may be two propellers, one under each wing connected for instance to the motor by shafting and bevel gearing or in 40 any other convenient manner. Or if convenient the engine and the propeller may be in close proximity. Although I have shown the engine and the propeller with their axes in the same plane, this is not essential as the axes may be in different planes and motion may be transmitted from the engine as aforesaid by means of bevel or other gearing. The main frame consists of two masts C placed 45 from about 6 to 10 feet apart according to the size of the machine, each having a total height of about 6 to 8 feet and standing vertical or approximately vertical when the wings are horizontal. The said masts C are connected to each other by an upper cross bar E at or near the top and below at or near the middle by a lower cross bar D preferably curved down slightly in the middle but if desired it may be made straight.

50 The junction between the masts may conveniently be effected by a metal jointing piece or double socket T.

There are also wires or rods 10 from the lower cross bar D to the bottom of the masts C and wires 9 to the upper cross bar E at or near its junctions with the masts which wires are best seen in Fig. 3. There may also be wires 12 from the centre of the cross bar E to the tops of the masts.

There is a fore and aft body piece F F composed of two pieces of bamboo, wood or steel tube, connected together at the ends by being held in suitable cast sockets I and J or in any other convenient manner. 5

The aëronaut takes up his position in the body piece F F, the width of which is about 20 inches for an ordinary sized man but may be more or less according to his size, one of the bamboos F being on each side. To each of these bamboos F there is attached a vertical handle G which the aëronaut holds in his hands and about a foot abaft of these handles are two straps, loops or tubes H which are padded and through which his fore arms pass so that when carrying the machine he takes the weight chiefly by means of the straps H and is able to tilt it as he wishes by means of the handles G. When he is resting on the machine his weight is taken on the padding under the straps, or on the body piece and holding tightly on to the handles he is able to move the weight of his body forwards and backwards so as to balance the machine in a fore and aft direction when it is supported in the air. In order to prevent the straps from bending outwards they are suitably provided with a lashing or support H^1 see Figures 3 and 4. 10 15

The body piece F F rests on the lower cross bar D of the main frame and is held to it by lashings or by other means. From the ends of this body piece wires 11 are attached to the tops and bottoms of the masts and keep them from moving in a fore and aft direction. The wings A are stiffened by means of a number of spokes K radiating from each of the masts C just above the junction with the lower cross piece. These spokes are made preferably of bamboo but other materials such as straight grained wood or steel tubing may be substituted. 20 25

These spokes K are stayed or braced by means of wires Y leading to the tops of the masts and wires Z leading to the bottoms of the masts or to some suitable connections at or near the tops S and bottoms S^1 of the masts.

There are preferably two wires from the shorter of the spokes to the top and two wires to the bottom of each mast but in the case of the longer spokes there are three wires to the top and three to the bottom of the mast from each spoke K, but there may be more or less. 30

The connection of each spoke to the mast is made by a metal piece not shown in the form of a loop or eye attached to the spoke and passing completely round the mast but allowing sufficient freedom for the spoke to be revolved round the mast. The spokes are kept in position on the mast by their loops resting on the top of the socket T and are lashed down by lashings. Or the spokes may be mounted in a bracket parallel with the mast. 35

In each wing there are 8 or 9 spokes which or some of which pass through pockets M (see Figure 4) sewn on to the underside of the wing confining it to the spokes and keeping the latter from being bent or sprung sideways. The wing is attached to the end of each spoke K by means of a lashing V made between an eye K^1 in the end of the spoke and loops made of tape in suitable positions on the wings but these connections may also be effected in any other convenient manner. 40 45

The sail is preferably strengthened by tapes or other material and patches L where the loops are made.

As the spokes pass through the pockets M under the wings, the wires Y from the spokes K to the tops S of the masts must necessarily pass through the wings. In order that the said wires shall not tear the wings when they pass through, a hole one to three inches in diameter is cut through the wings for each wire, and the holes are strengthened by cementing a patch of sail cloth or other material all round same so as to keep the wires from tearing the wings. The patch may be varnished over afterwards if desired. 50 55

The wings are made of closely woven cotton or other similar material but goldbeaters' skin may be used.

The width over the wing tips of the whole machine is from about twenty to thirty feet and the length fore and aft over wings from about seven to twelve feet. These sizes will vary with the weight of the aëronaut the amount of wind in the case of soaring machines, and the speed at which it is intended to drive in 5 the case of flying machines having motive power.

The front of the body piece F F extends a foot or so in front of the forward edge of the wings so that it will receive the blow in the event of the machine striking anything end on and also to form a sort of bowsprit to give the wires 11 from the forward end of the body piece F F to the mast heads S a better lead, as 10 the main frame is in front of the centre of the body piece.

The wings A are laced to the body piece F F as shown only on the right hand side of Figure 4 and each sail is divided from the mast to the body piece and the two edges are laced with a lacing *x* when the wing is extended or set. But if the lacings X and X¹ are cast off the whole of the spokes K and the wings are free to 15 revolve round the masts and to be furled. The wings are slightly curved both fore and aft and transversely and so as to be concave on the lower side. The fore and aft curvature is given because at small angles to the wind the lifting power is greater for the same resistance to forward motion, and the longitudinal balance can be more easily controlled for the longitudinal shift of the centre of lift is less in 20 the case of a suitably curved surface than it is in the case of a plane or flat surface.

The transverse curvature of the wings is such that the body piece is lowest; each wing rises towards its centre and drops again towards its tip, the tip being preferably about six inches to a foot above the body piece F F.

25 The rudder B has preferably transverse surface only as shewn, but it may have a vertical surface or blade also. The transverse surface of the rudder is slightly inclined to the wing surface as shewn on Figs. 1 and 2.

The surface of the transverse rudder is about one tenth of the area of the surface of the wings, that is to say, if the wing area is 170 square feet, the transverse 30 rudder surface will be about 17 square feet. These proportions however may be modified in particular machines in order to counteract a particular distribution of weight in a fore and aft direction.

The rudder B is attached to the after end of the body piece F F by means of a shaft O which is pivoted for instance to the socket or part I in such manner that 35 it cannot be depressed relatively to the wings and so that on alighting, if the part Q of the rudder strike the ground or other obstacle it will simply move on its pivot and take no great shock and when the machine is in the air it will enable the aëronaut by throwing his weight back on the machine to cause the latter to rise in front or tilt up more quickly than would be the case if the rudder were not 40 free to move. The rudder cannot be depressed and therefore the transverse surface will keep the machine from pitching suddenly forward.

The rudder is kept from moving sideways by means of lines 7, 7, shown only on the left hand side of Figure 4 going from the extremities of two of the spokes K in the after sides of the wings and from depression by lines 6, 6, attached to the 45 mast C or cross bar E. The rudder is further stayed or distended by being made on a light frame P, Q and R.

The steering is effected by inclining the weight of the body to the right or left respectively if one desires to turn to the right or left.

Having now particularly described and ascertained the nature of my said inven-50 tion, and in what manner the same is to be performed, I declare that what I claim is :—

1. A soaring machine consisting of a body piece with loops H and handles G cross bars D E and masts C on which are mounted wings A stiffened by spokes K with wires for giving rigidity and a pivoted rudder or tail B substantially as 55 described and shewn.

2. A flying machine consisting of a body piece with loops H and handles G,

cross bars D E and masts C on which are mounted wings A stiffened by spokes K with wires for giving rigidity, a pivoted rudder or tail B, and an engine or motor driving a propeller substantially as described and shewn.

3. In a flying or soaring machine the construction of wings A mounted on spokes K and stayed by wires Y and Z substantially as described and shewn. 5

4. In a flying or soaring machine the construction of wings A mounted on spokes K capable of revolving on the masts C to permit of furling the wings said wings being stayed by wires Y and Z substantially as described and shewn.

5. In a flying or soaring machine the construction of wings A having pockets M for the purpose of confirming the wings to the spokes and preventing the latter 10 from bending substantially as described and shewn.

6. In a flying or soaring machine the employment of travelling wheels 3 adapted to yield perpendicularly and to a slight extent in the fore and aft direction in the event of their striking the earth or an obstacle in order to lessen the jar to the 15 machine substantially as described and shewn.

7. The constructions of soaring and flying machines shown on the drawings.

Dated this Twenty-second day of January 1897.

JENSEN & SON,
77 Chancery Lane, London, W.C., Patent Agents.

London : Printed for Her Majesty's Stationery Office, by Darling & Son, Ltd.—1897

[This Drawing is a reproduction of the Original on a reduced scale]

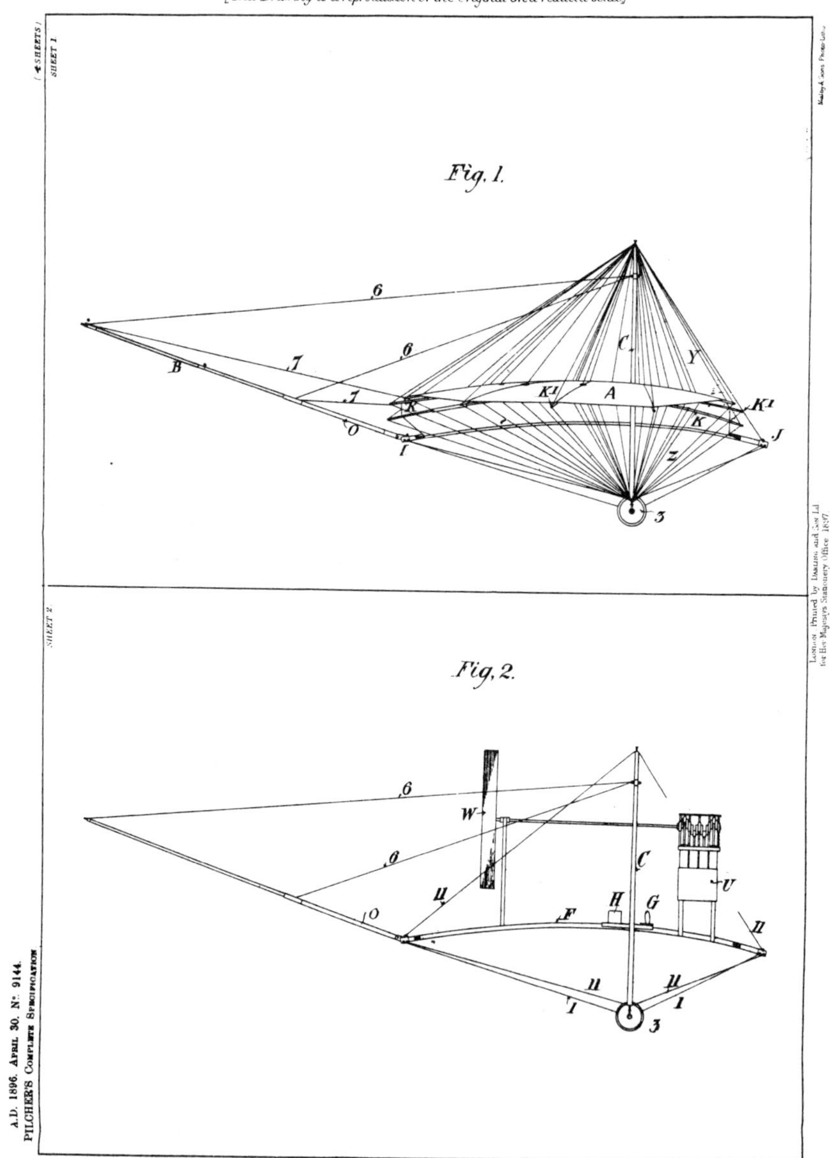

A.D. 1896. APRIL 30. N°. 9144.
PILCHER'S COMPLETE SPECIFICATION.

(4 SHEETS)
SHEET 3.

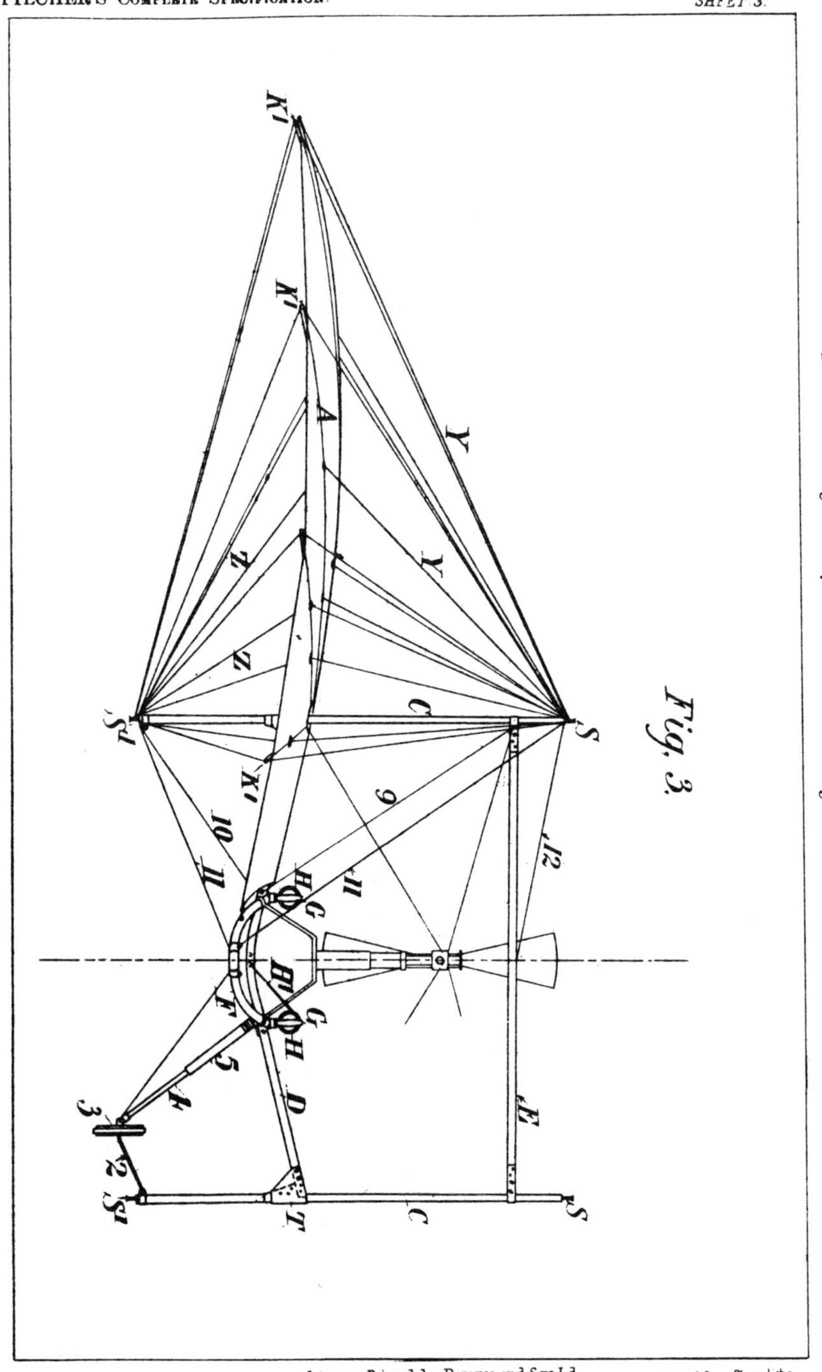

[This Drawing is a reproduction of the Original on a reduced scale]

LONDON. Printed by DARLING and SON Ld.
for Her Majesty's Stationery Office. 1897

Malby & Sons, Photo-Litho.

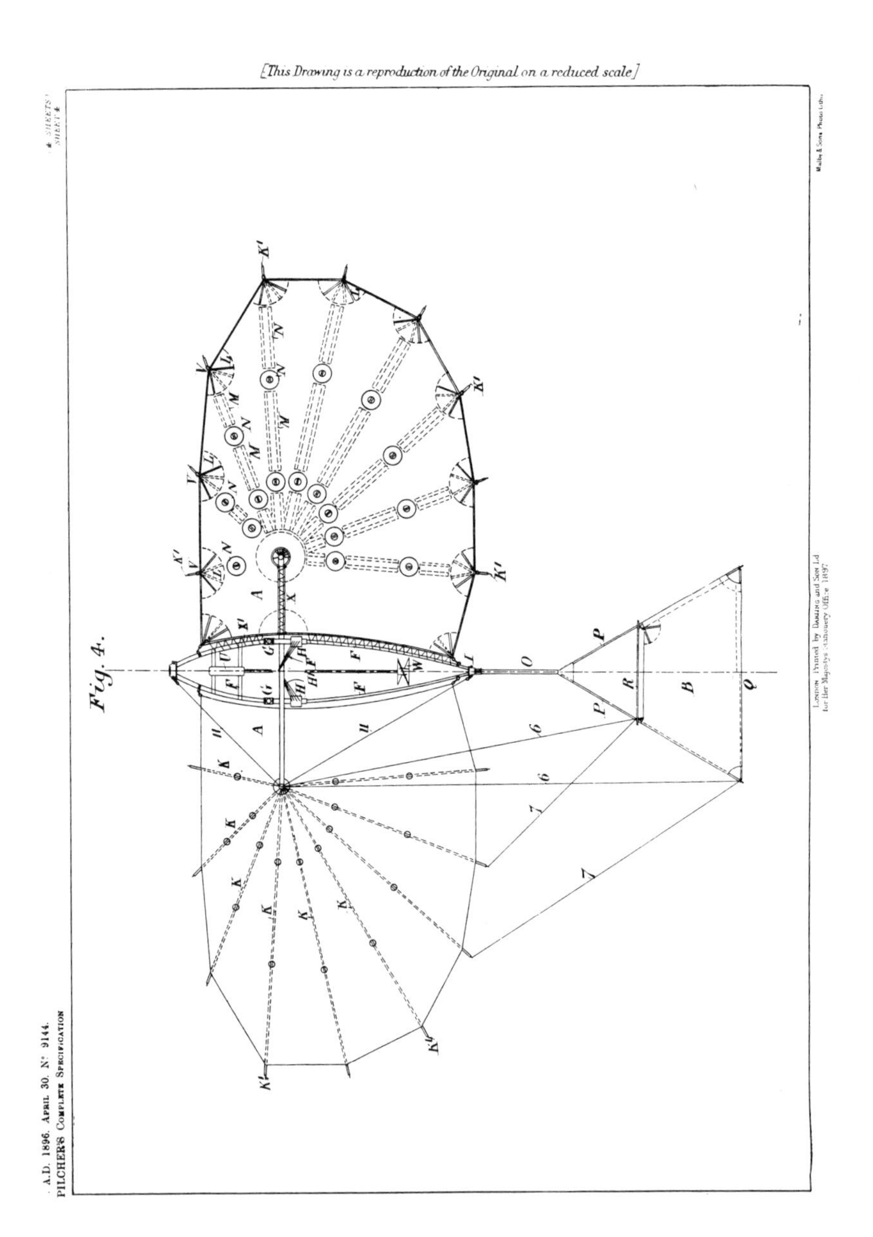
[This Drawing is a reproduction of the Original on a reduced scale]
A.D. 1896. April 30. N° 9144.
PILCHER'S Complete Specification
Fig. 4.
London Printed by Darling and Son Ltd for Her Majesty's Stationery Office 1897

N° 29,194  A.D. 1896

Date of Application, 19th Dec., 1896
Complete Specification Left, 20th Sept., 1897—Accepted, 11th Dec., 1897

PROVISIONAL SPECIFICATION.

"Improvements in Sails for Boats and other Vessels, and in Means for Setting, Working, and Furling same."

We, WALTER GORDON WILSON of Dunardagh Blackrock in the County of Dublin, Engineer and PERCY SINCLAIR PILCHER of Artillery Mansions, Victoria Street in the City of Westminster Engineer do hereby declare the nature of this invention to be as follows:—

5 Our invention relates to sails for boats and other vessels and to means for setting working and furling same.

According to our invention we mount the sail at right angles to the mast or approximately at right angles thereto, the latter passing to or through the centre of the sail or thereabouts and the mast is made capable of being revolved and of being 10 inclined more or less to the vertical. The sail in fact may be popularly described as being more or less in the form of an umbrella, the stick forming the mast. The sail is preferably mounted on ribs supported by stretchers or ties or both which are secured to the mast in such manner as to permit of the sail being furled or lowered in any convenient manner. The mast which is on a universal joint may conveniently 15 be raised and lowered and fixed at any inclination and either pointing forward or on either side of the boat by means of tackles or other gear but preferably we mount the mast very much in the way that the jib of a crane is mounted, that is to say it is pivotted away from the central pivot or so called "Samson Post" and is provided with gear such as worm and worm wheel or chain and chain wheels or the like for 20 revolving the mast and the mast may be raised and lowered by means of a tackle.

The weight of the mast and sail may conveniently be counterbalanced by a weight or weights or by a spring or springs or by both.

In beating or with the wind on the beam this is a distinct advantage because the pull then by the sail is upward from the lee side and not from the side to windward 25 of the keel whereby the chances of a capsize are practically removed. The mast is preferably not mounted in the centre of the sail but at some little distance therefrom in such manner that there is more sail area on the side nearest the water than there is on the side furthest away and this gives more lifting power to the lee side of the vessel than to the windward side. We may make the sail approximately circular, 30 but we prefer to make it somewhat in the form of an oval or an ellipse. The sail instead of being at a normal angle to the mast may also be made capable of being moved angularly to the mast to permit of the sail being set at any desired angle including also vertically when sailing with a very light breeze whereby the whole area of the sail becomes effective. Under ordinary circumstances when the sail is 35 set at an angle to the vertical the whole force of the wind on the sail is not available for driving the boat but part of the force serves to lift the boat thereby causing her to ride more easily than is the case with vessels propelled by ordinary sails. It follows also that the nearer the sail is set to the horizontal position the less effect the wind will have on it.

Dated this 19th day of Dec. 1896.

JENSEN & SON
77 Chancery Lane London W.C. Patent Agents. 5

COMPLETE SPECIFICATION.

"Improvements in Sails for Boats and other Vessels, and in Means for Setting, Working, and Furling same."

We, WALTER GORDON WILSON of Dunardagh Blackrock in the County of Dublin Engineer and PERCY SINCLAIR PILCHER of Artillery Mansions, Victoria Street in the 10 City of Westminster, Engineer, do hereby declare the nature of this invention and in what manner the same is to be performed to be particularly described and ascertained in and by the following statement:—

Our invention relates to sails for boats and other vessels and to means for setting working and furling same. 15

According to our invention we mount the sail at right angles to the mast or approximately at right angles thereto, the latter passing to or through the centre of the sail or thereabouts and the mast is made capable of being revolved or turned in any direction and of being inclined more or less to the vertical. The sail in fact may be described in popular language as being more or less in the form of an 20 umbrella, the stick forming the mast.

Figure 1 of the accompanying drawings represents in elevation a simple construction of sail applied to a boat.

Figure 2 is a perspective view of a boat shewing the application of the sail shewn in detail in Figure 8 and the mast shewn in Figures 9 and 10. 25

Figure 3 represents in elevation a convenient and simple method of mounting a mast to be used with a sail constructed according to our invention.

Figure 4 is a sectional plan thereof on the line 3—3 with the grooved disc A and Samson Post removed.

Figure 5 is a plan. 30

Figure 6 is a sectional elevation on the line 5—5 Figure 3 and

Figure 7 is a plan of the foot B.

Figure 8 is a plan of one construction of sail, one half of the sail that is on the right hand side thereof being shown set, while the other half on the left hand side is shown furled or housed. 35

Figure 9 is a transverse section through a boat showing a modified arrangement for supporting and regulating the position of the mast and

Figure 10 is a plan thereof.

Referring to Figure 1 it will be seen that the Sail C is made somewhat in the form of an umbrella with ribs designated by the letter D the whole being mounted on the 40 mast E by means of a runner F which is made to slide up when the sail is to be furled as illustrated by the dotted lines. The mast E is pivotted in the boat at G and is capable of being lowered in any direction and at any angle or inclination to the vertical. The sail is stayed and kept as nearly as possible rigid by means of a number of stays L and M attached to the ribs D and to the mast. If desired the 45 sail may be provided with a number of stretchers as is an ordinary umbrella whereby a great many or all of the stays or guy ropes L and M can be dispensed with. The mast E may conveniently be raised and lowered and fixed at any inclination and either pointing forward or on either side of the boat by means of tackles K.

We prefer however to mount the mast E very much in the way that the jib of a 50 crane is mounted and Figures 3 to 7 inclusive illustrate a simple construction of this kind. There is a foot or bed B made capable of attachment to the kelson of the boat or to a suitable framing or bed therein and to this foot is attached or fixed a kind of so called " Samson post " B^1 made hollow for the sake of lightness. Outside of this and capable of revolving thereon is a sleeve E^1 to which is fixed a frame consisting of two pieces E^2 Figure 3 and in dotted lines in Figure 4 and two quadrant shaped pieces E^3 one of which is shown as provided with an extension or handle E^4. The mast E is pivotted at E^5 to the frame E^1, E^2 E^3 E^4 and when the desired inclination has been obtained by hand it is clamped on the quadrant shaped parts E^3 of the frame by its clamps E^6 operated by the hand screw E^7. The Samson Post B^1 has fixed thereon a grooved disc A and the handle part of the frame E^1 E^2 E^3 is provided with a set screw E^8 the point of which takes into the groove of the disc A. The mast is moved to any desired position either pointing forward or more or less on either side of the boat and when in position the set screw E^8 is tightened and jambs it there.

Referring to figure 8 which shews in detail one modification of sail C it will be seen that there is a kind of trussed girder or yard C^1 made principally of bamboo or of other light material which is clamped to the mast by a bracket C^2 preferably made of aluminium on the score of lightness. The sail C in this case is preferably so arranged with regard to the mast E that its centre does not coincide with the centre of the mast in such manner that there is more sail area on the side nearest the water than there is on the other side furthest away and this causes the wind to apply more lifting power to the lee side of the vessel than to the windward side. The sail might be made circular as indicated in Figure 1 but we may also divide it into two parts and to make it somewhat in the form of an oval or an ellipse as shewn in Figures 2 and 8. The sail is mounted on a number of ribs D and D^1 which sets of ribs are respectively pivotted to the pins or bolts D^2 so that the sail may be furled as snugly as possible when not in use and as indicated by the left hand side of Figure 8 but it should be noted that on that side of the figure the housed sail with its ribs are broken off owing to the limited space on the drawing. The halves of the sail are on one side of the mast E laced to light ribs or battens C^3 pivotted as are the ribs D and these battens are connected by running gear C^6 to the girder or yard C^1 and down the mast as will be evident without further description. The other sides of each half of the sail are merely laced to the yard C^1 as shown. To furl or house the sail there is attached to each half thereof a tricing line C^4 which is fixed to a batten C^3 and goes through some rings on the ribs D and D^1 through a block down to a cleat on the mast or in any other convenient place. If it be desired to house the sail the running gear C^6 is slacked off the tricing lines are pulled and the two halves of the sail are closely stowed as shown on the left hand side of the Figure 8.

Figure 2 shows a convenient way of holding the sail rigid on the mast. It consists in providing a number of guys or stays L from at or near the top of the mast or from more than one place on the mast above the sail to one two or more places on each rib and similarly a number of guys or stays M from a point or points below the sail and on the mast to one or more places on each rib. For convenience in attaching the stays L and M to the ribs the sail is at each place provided with a hole N, the material of the sail being strengthened or reinforced by means of a patch or otherwise if necessary.

Figures 9 and 10 show an arrangement of gear for actuating the mast where the sail is larger and not capable of being so easily handled as in the arrangement shown in Figures 3 to 7 as before the mast E is pivotted to a post E^1 and it may be raised by means of a tackle K^1 and lowered by a tackle K^2 attached to the post in a kind of hatch or turntable K^3 which is capable of revolving on or round a coaming or other support O on the boat or vessel. This turntable has a slot for the mast to travel in as shown and it is capable of being revolved either by hand or by suitable gearing and clamped by a screw or other clamp E^8 in any position. The weight of the mast and sail may conveniently be counterbalanced by a spring or springs or by a weight P pivotted in such manner as to be most effectual when the mast is most inclined. The weight is connected to the mast by means of a rope or chain going over pulleys P^1 P^2. Instead of using a weight or spring only the weight of the mast may be counteracted by means of a combination of a spring and a weight. Q Q are stays for holding the post in position.

The sail, instead of being fixed at a normal angle to the mast may also be made capable of being moved angularly to the mast to permit of the sail being set at any desired angle including also vertically when sailing with a very light breeze whereby the whole area of the sail becomes effective. Under ordinary circumstances when the sail is set at an angle to the vertical the whole force of the wind on the sail is not available for driving the vessel but part of the force serves to lift the vessel thereby causing her to ride more easily than in the case with vessels propelled by ordinary sails. It follows also that the nearer the sail is set to the horizontal position the less effect the wind will have on it and under most circumstances a vessel may be anchored or lie hove to with the sail in the horizontal position without making sternway appreciably.

Having now particularly described and ascertained the nature of our said invention and in what manner the same is to be performed we declare that what we claim is:—

1. A sail for a boat or other vessel kept in shape by a nnmber of ribs radiating from at or near the centre of the mast and adapted to be set in any position relatively to the vessel substantially as set forth.

2. A sail for a boat or other vessel adapted to be kept in shape by a number of ribs D D^1 mounted on a bracket C^2 attached to a mast E having guys or stays L M substantially as described and shown.

3. Means for setting sails as firstly and secondly claimed consisting of a mast E pivotted to a universal joint in the vessel and gear for regulating the position of the mast and holding it in the desired position substantially as described and shown.

4. Means for setting sails as firstly or secondly claimed consisting of a mast E pivotted to or near a samson post E^1 mounted in the vessel and gear for regulating the inclination of the mast and holding same in the desired position substantially as described and shown.

5. The constructions of sails and gear for setting working and furling or housing same substantially as described and shown on the drawings.

Dated this Twentieth day of Septr. 1897.

JENSEN & SON
77 Chancery Lane London W.C. Patent Agents.

Redhill: Printed for Her Majesty's Stationery Office, by Malcomson & Co., Ltd.—1897.

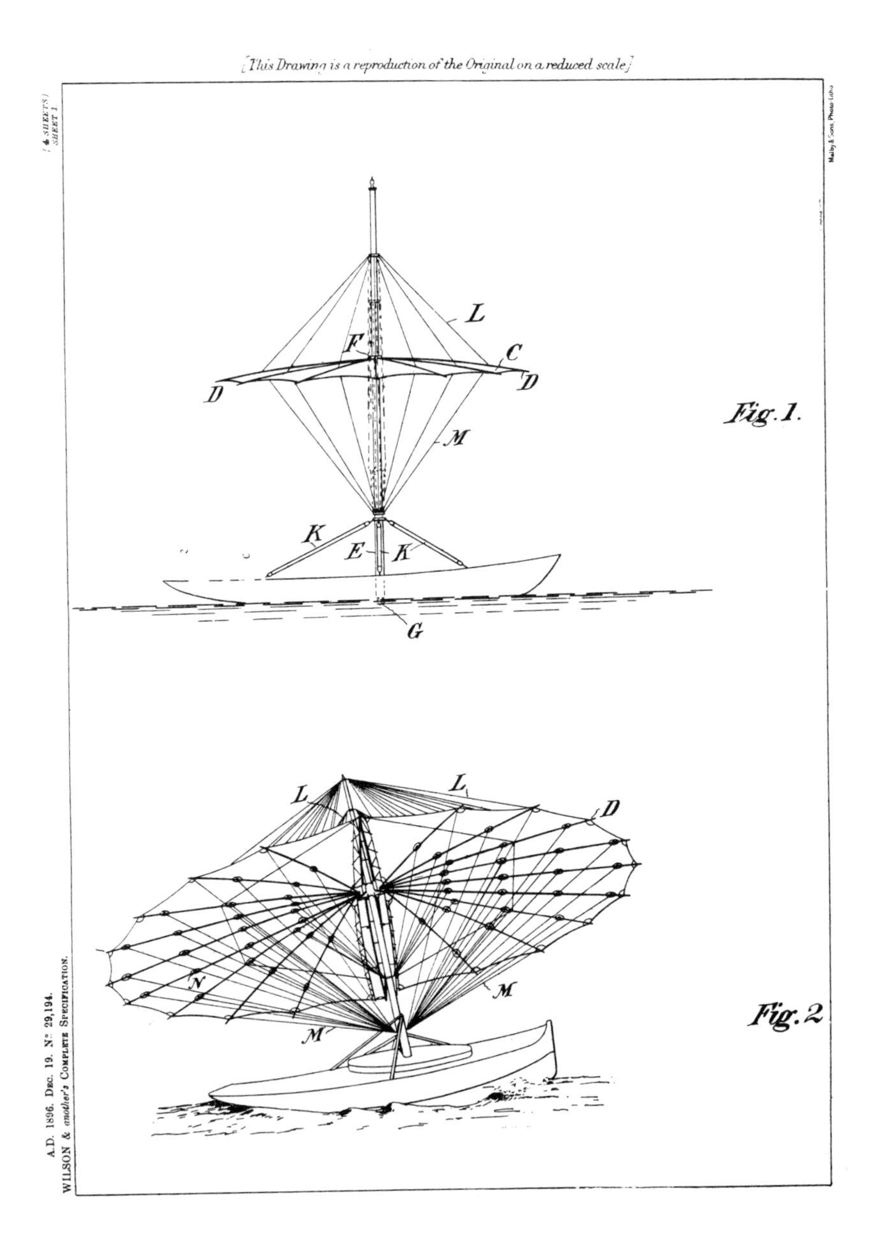
[This Drawing is a reproduction of the Original on a reduced scale]
SHEET 1
Malby & Sons, Photo-Litho
L
F
C
D
D
M
K
E
K
G
Fig. 1.
L
L
D
N
M
M
Fig. 2
A.D. 1896. Dec. 19. No 29,194.
WILSON & another's Complete Specification.

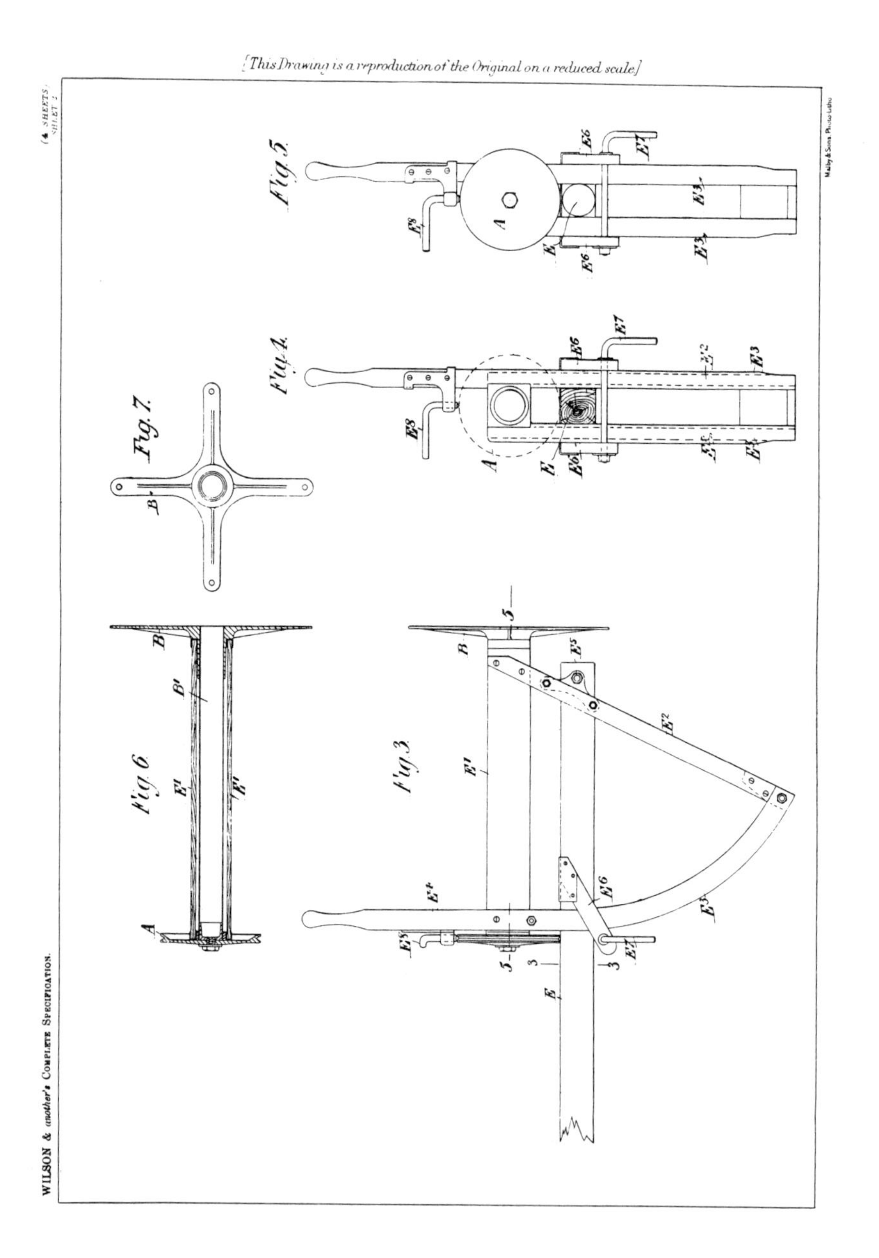
[This Drawing is a reproduction of the Original on a reduced scale]
WILSON & another's COMPLETE SPECIFICATION.
(4 SHEETS) SHEET 2
Fig. 3
Fig. 4
Fig. 5
Fig. 6
Fig. 7

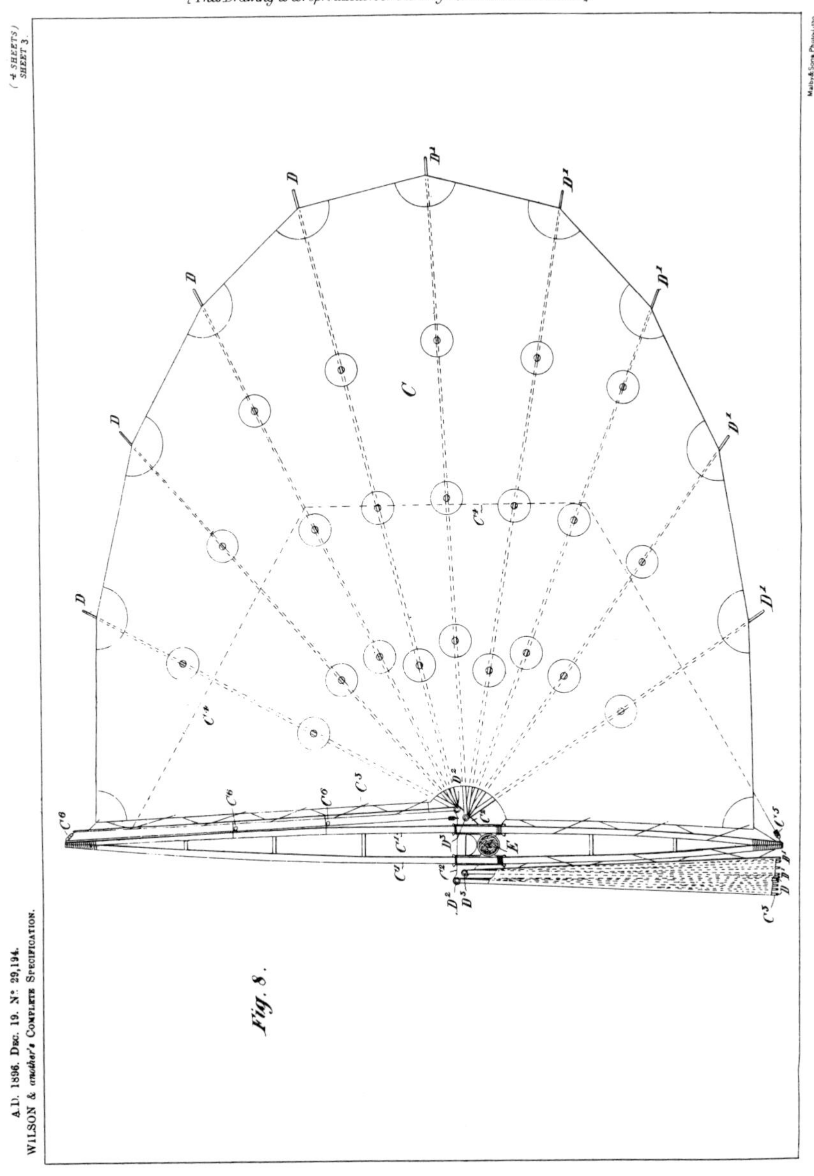
[This Drawing is a reproduction of the Original on a reduced scale.]
A.D. 1896. Dec. 19. N° 29,194.
WILSON & another's Complete Specification.
(4 SHEETS)
SHEET 3.
Fig. 8.
C
D
D¹
D²
D³
E
C²
C³
C⁴
C⁵
C⁶
Malby & Sons, Photo-Litho

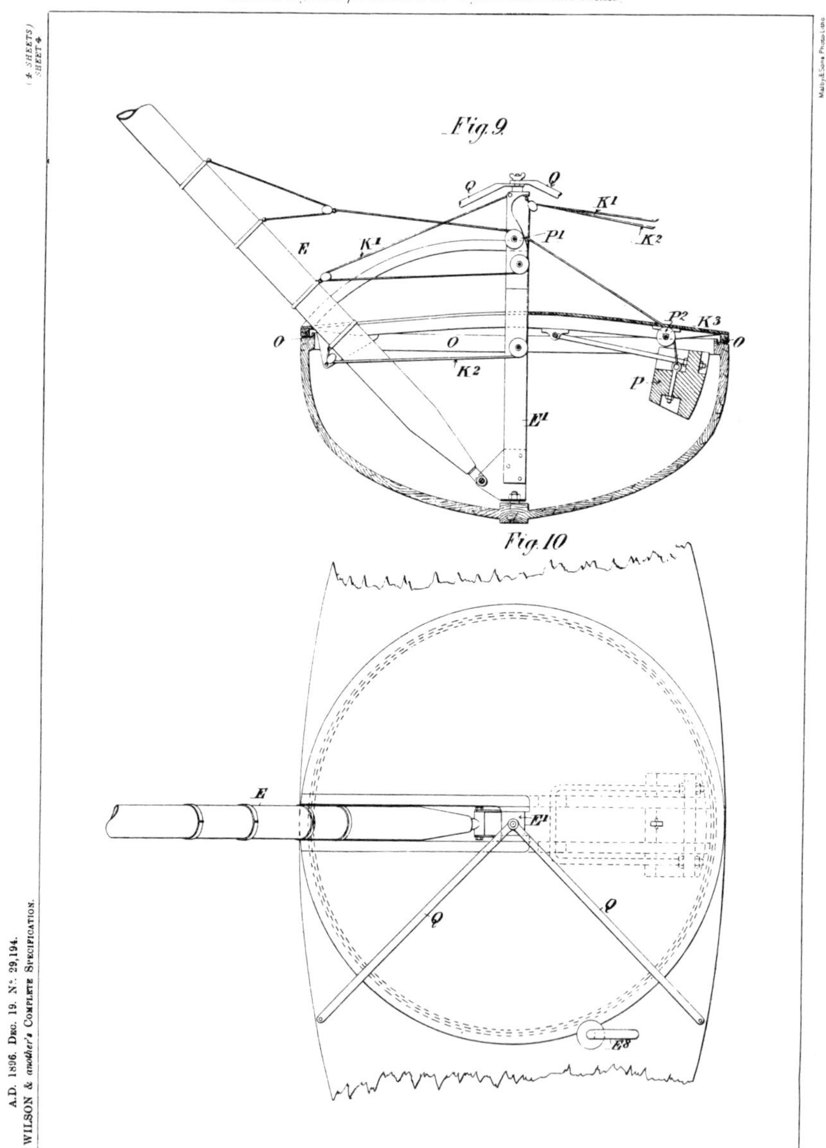
This Drawing is a reproduction of the Original on a reduced scale.
(4 SHEETS)
SHEET 4
Fig. 9
Q
Q
K1
K2
P1
E
K1
P2
K3
O
O
O
K2
P
E1
Fig. 10
E
E1
Q
Q
E8
A.D. 1896. DEC. 19. No. 29,194.
WILSON & another's COMPLETE SPECIFICATION.

N° 11,619  A.D. 1897

Date of Application, 10th May, 1897

Complete Specification Left, 10th Mar., 1898—Accepted, 16th Apr., 1898

PROVISIONAL SPECIFICATION.

Improvements in and connected with Engines actuated by Mixed Products of Combustion and Steam.

I, Percy Sinclair Pilcher, of Artillery Mansions, Victoria Street, in the City of Westminster and County of Middlesex, Gentleman, do hereby declare the nature of this invention to be as follows:—

My invention consists in a new or improved motive power engine which is
5 operated by the gases resulting from steam and the combustion of oil, spirit, gas or other inflammable material together with air or the like for supporting such combustion.

I may conveniently construct an engine to operate according to my invention as follows:—

10 I provide a boiler having a fireplace or furnace, inside of which is a coil, one end of which latter communicates with the water space in the boiler and the level of the water therein is kept as nearly as possible constantly full or at some other desired level. Water is constantly pumped into or caused to enter the boiler and as soon as it is above the level of the pipe leading to the coil it flows into same. As
15 an example the furnace may be fired by means of oil or gaseous fuel and the necessary air for supporting the combustion thereof is conveniently introduced by means of an air compressor, the air being warmed or not as desired before it enters the furnace. The air suitably passes through a kind of injector and induces the supply of oil or vapour which is also conveniently admitted under pressure and the
20 burning gases serve to heat the water in the coil to form steam which passes out by a jet into the furnace or into a pipe in communication therewith so as to induce a current. The products of combustion and the steam therefore pass out of the furnace by the aforesaid pipe (either directly or indirectly after being purified, if this should be necessary) to the cylinder of the engine, which is provided with a
25 water jacket and valves for the inlet and exhaust of the working fluid. The piston of the engine may directly operate the air compressor or the latter may be operated indirectly. As a matter of convenience the water which serves to cool the engine may be conducted to the boiler to be ultimately turned into steam. If desired the engine and the compressor may be wholly enclosed by a water jacket the crank
30 shaft being provided with stuffing boxes to prevent leakage or only those parts are enclosed which are most subjected to heat or require a certain amount of cooling such as the compressor. If hot air is to be pumped into the furnace it is conveniently heated after leaving the compressor.

Dated this 10th day of May 1897.

35 JENSEN & SON,
77, Chancery Lane, London, W.C., Patent Agents.

COMPLETE SPECIFICATION.

Improvements in and connected with Engines actuated by Mixed Products of Combustion and Steam.

I, PERCY SINCLAIR PILCHER, late of Artillery Mansions, Victoria Street, in the City of Westminster, Gentleman, but now of Wilson & Pilcher Limited, of 17, Mount Pleasant, Grays Inn Road, in the County of Middlesex, Managing Director, do hereby declare the nature of this invention and in what manner the same is to be performed to be particularly described and ascertained in and by the following statement:— 5

My invention consists in a new or improved motive power engine, which is operated by the gases resulting from steam and the combustion of oil spirit gas or other inflammable material, together with air or the like for supporting such combustion. 10

I may conveniently construct an engine to operate according to my invention as follows:—

I provide a boiler having a fireplace or furnace inside of which is a coil, one end of which latter communicates with the water space in the boiler and the level of the water therein is kept as nearly as possible constantly full or at some other desired level. Water is constantly pumped into or caused to enter the boiler and as soon as it is above the level of the pipe leading to the coil it flows into same. As an example the furnace may be fired by means of oil or gaseous fuel and the necessary air for supporting the combustion thereof is conveniently introduced by means of an air compressor, the air being warmed or not as desired before it enters the furnace. The air suitably passes through a kind of injector and induces the supply of oil or vapour which is also conveniently admitted under pressure and the burning gases serve to heat the water in the coil to form steam which passes out by a jet into the furnace or into a pipe in communication therewith. The products of combustion and the steam therefore pass out of the furnace by the aforesaid pipe (either directly or indirectly after being purified, if this should be necessary) to the cylinder of the engine, which is provided with a water jacket and valves for the inlet and exhaust of the working fluid. The piston of the engine may directly operate the air compressor or the latter may be operated indirectly. As a matter of convenience the water which serves to cool the engine may be conducted to the boiler to be ultimately converted into steam. 15 20 25 30

If desired, the engine and the compressor may be wholly enclosed by a water jacket, the crank shaft being provided with stuffing boxes to prevent leakage or only those parts are enclosed which are most subjected to heat or require a certain amount of cooling such as the compressor. 35

If hot air is to be pumped into the furnace it is conveniently heated after leaving the compressor.

On the accompanying sheet of drawings I have shown in section one convenient construction of engine and boiler to operate according to my invention. A is the shell of the boiler which may be cylindrical as shown or of any other desirable form provided with a furnace or combustion chamber B. Within the combustion chamber B is placed a coil C which may be of any convenient form or size, or extending, as shown upon the drawings, across and near the crown of the combustion chamber. One end C^1 of the coil C communicates with the water space A^1 of the boiler, which is kept as nearly as possible constantly full of water or with water at some other desired level. Water is constantly pumped into or caused to enter the water space A^1 of the boiler by means of a pipe A^2 and as soon as it is 40 45 above the level of the end C^1 of the coil C it flows into same, or if desired only steam may enter the end of the pipe C^1.

As an example the furnace or combustion chamber B may be fired by means of oil or gaseous fuel which enters by a pipe or pipes E and nozzle or nozzles E^1 into
5 a mixing chamber F in the bottom of the furnace B the necessary air for supporting the combustion thereof being conveniently introduced by means of the air compressor G or otherwise and the air being warmed or not as desired before it enters the furnace. One convenient way of warming the air from the air compressor before it enters the furnace is to enclose the shell of the boiler in a casing H
10 so as to leave an air space H^1 between the two, the air from the air compressor G passing by a pipe G^1 into the said air space whence it is conducted by a pipe or coil H^2 into the mixing chamber F.

The air under pressure may suitably pass through a kind of injector (not shewn) so as to induce a supply of oil or vapour or
15 the oil or vapour may also be conveniently admitted under pressure into the mixing chamber F. The burning gases serve to heat the water in the boiler A and also to superheat or dry the steam or water in the coil C so that steam passes out by a jet or nozzle C^2 into the combustion chamber B or into a pipe B^1 in communication therewith and passes through the top of the boiler. If
20 desired the coil C may be dispensed with and the pipe C^1 may lead directly to the nozzle C^2 or direct into the pipe B, and the steam mixing with the products of combustion becomes superheated or dried. The products of combustion and the steam therefore pass out of the combustion chamber B by the pipe B^1 (either directly or indirectly after being purified, if this should be necessary) and the pipe B^2
25 to the cylinder K of the engine which is provided with a water jacket L and valves J^1 J^2 for the inlet and exhaust respectively of the working fluid. I may also provide a perforated pipe or pipes B^3 to permit some of the products of combustion to penetrate the water space A^1 in the boiler and thereby increase the evaporating power of the combustion chamber B. Besides this the effect will be
30 that some of the products of combustion are more or less scrubbed or purified.

The piston M of the engine may directly operate the air compressing piston N or the latter may be operated indirectly. As a matter of convenience the water enters by a pipe O through the water jacket P of the air compressing cylinder G thence by a pipe Q to the water jacket L of the engine and may be conducted by
35 a pipe A^2 to the water space A^1 of the boiler to be ultimately turned into steam.

S is an air inlet pipe to the air compressing cylinder and T is an exhaust pipe from the engine.

It is evident that the water and the combustible oil or gas must be forced in under pressure either by a pump or pumps operated by the engine or in any other
40 convenient manner.

Having now particularly described and ascertained the nature of my said invention and in what manner the same is to be performed I declare that what I claim is:—

1. An engine actuated by mixed products of combustion and steam provided with
45 a boiler having an internal combustion chamber in which the products of combustion are produced under pressure and connections from the combustion chamber and from the boiler to the cylinder of the engine so that the steam is superheated or dried before performing its work substantially as described and shewn.

2. An engine actuated by mixed products of combustion and steam provided
50 with a boiler having a combustion chamber in which the products of combustion are produced under pressure, connections from the combustion chamber and from the boiler to the cylinder of the engine and means for heating the air used to support the combustion substantially as described and shewn.

3. An engine actuated by mixed products of combustion and steam having a
55 jacket surrounding its cylinder through which passes water for cooling purposes

and provided with a boiler fed by the warm water proceeding from the said water jacket, said boiler having a combustion chamber in which the products of combustion are produced under pressure, connections from the combustion chamber and from the boiler to the cylinder of the engine and means for heating the air used to support combustion substantially as described and shown. 5

4. An engine actuated by mixed products of combustion and steam provided with a boiler having a combustion chamber in which the products of combustion are produced under pressure, a perforated pipe or pipes leading from the combustion chamber to the boiler, connections from the combustion chamber and from the boiler to the cylinder of the engine and means for heating the air used to 10 support the combustion substantially as described and shewn.

5. An engine actuated by mixed products of combustion and steam provided with a boiler having a combustion chamber in which the products of combustion are produced under pressure, a connection from the combustion chamber to the engine and a coil passing from the boiler through the combustion chamber and thence 15 into the connection to the engine and means for heating the air used to support the combustion substantially as described and shown.

6. The construction shown on the drawing.

Dated this Tenth day of March 1898.

JENSEN & SON, 20
77, Chancery Lane, London, W.C., Patent Agents.

Redhill : Printed for Her Majesty's Stationery Office, by Malcomson & Co., Ltd.—1898

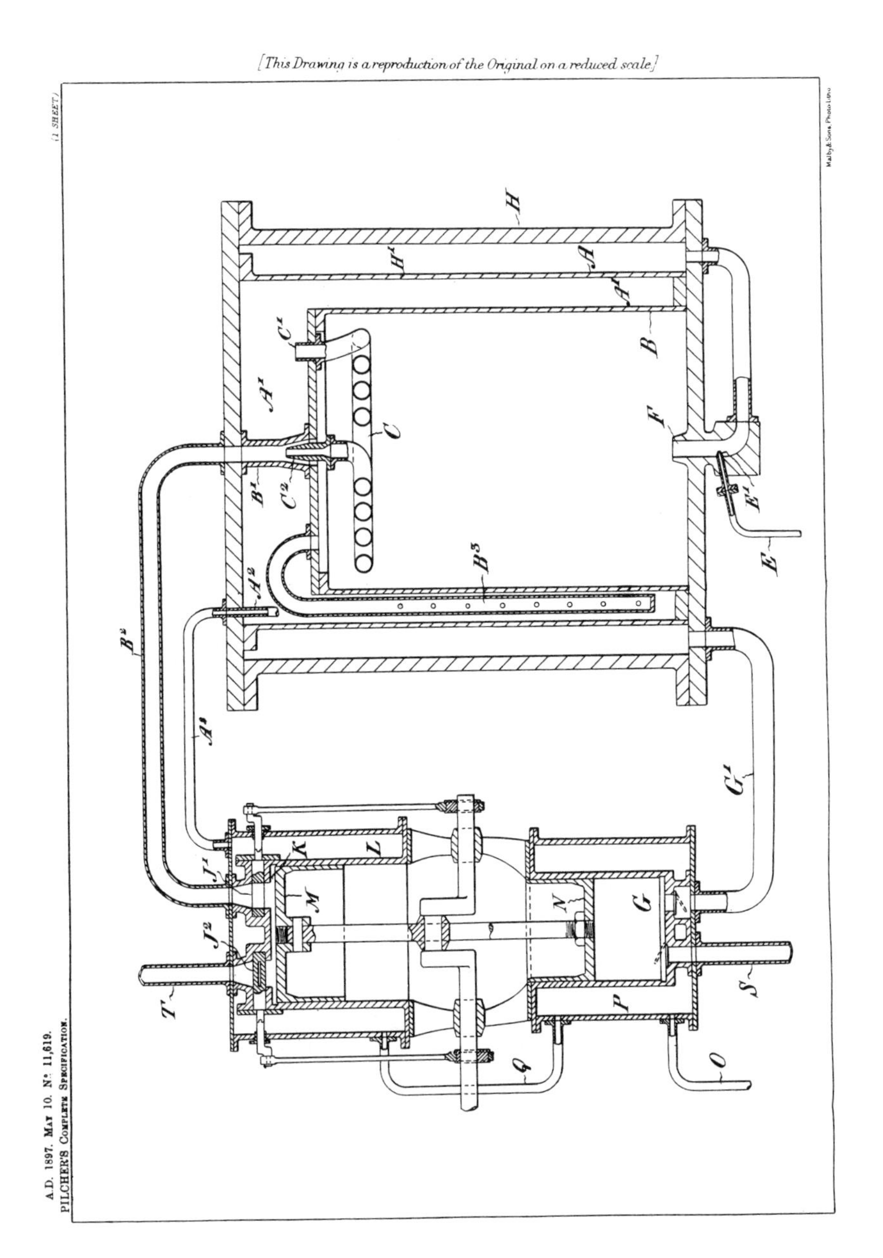
[This Drawing is a reproduction of the Original on a reduced scale.]
A.D. 1897. May 10. No. 11,619.
PILCHER'S Complete Specification.
(1 SHEET)
Malby & Sons, Photo-Litho

Appendix C

Wilson and Pilcher Limited

Following his partner's death, Walter Wilson kept Wilson and Pilcher going and concentrated on his first love—the gasoline-driven automobile. Adrian Verney Cave, also an enthusiastic motorist, joined the company as a new partner. While Wilson and Pilcher had been in their first workshops, in Clerkenwell, during 1897–98, Wilson had made a full-size wooden mockup of a small car, and had begun the design of a larger automobile.[1]

The first Wilson-Pilcher car to go into production appeared in 1901. It was a four-seater powered by a horizontally opposed four-cylinder engine, and was noted for "its almost entire freedom from noise or vibration."[2] Other features were the epicyclic gearbox, which permitted clutchless changes, and a flywheel with its arms shaped to enable it to serve as a fan to assist cooling. The prototype motor developed about 5 brake horsepower at 1,000 revolutions per minute, while 8 to 9 brake horsepower was anticipated for production units.

In 1903 a 10-horsepower four-seat model was produced, again incorporating many ingenious devices and systems devised by Wilson and again "eminently comfortable, noiseless, and vibrationless." Its "unusually large" flywheel again had pitched arms to double as a fan. It was pointed out that the large diameter and rim section of the flywheel were significant factors in the "wonderfully smooth running" of the engine.[3]

The following year a six-cylinder model of 18–24 horsepower was produced,[4] but by now the Newcastle engineering firm of Sir W. G.

Walter Wilson seated in a full-size wooden mockup of a small car, ca. 1898. (A. G. Wilson)

Armstrong, Whitworth and Co. had taken over production, and the firm of Wilson and Pilcher Limited was liquidated and dissolved during late 1904 and early 1905.[5]

The only known surviving example of a Wilson-Pilcher car, a 1904 model, is on show at the Tank Museum, Bovington, Dorset.

Appendix D

The Stanford Hall Memorial

Shortly after Pilcher's death the *Academy*, in its issue dated October 7, 1899, said; "Lord Braye, who is something of a poet and something of a theologian, thinks of raising a Pilcher monument in his park, with an inscription which his own pen is particularly well fitted to supply."

However, it was not until 1910 that the idea was followed up. In the October issue of the *Aeronautical Journal* (p. 167), appeared this letter:

> Sirs,—it has been proposed to erect a pillar as a memorial to the late Percy Pilcher, a pioneer of aviation. It would, perhaps, be correct to say *the* pioneer of aviation, for it was Pilcher who thought out and put into practice the project of gliding through the air with rigid wings, and he had the intention of propelling with a motor the machine he had made.
>
> Pilcher was the first Englishman to be killed in the cause of aviation, his fatal fall at Stanford Park, Market Harborough, taking place on September 30, 1899.
>
> Many who knew him and appreciated his self-devotion and zeal in promoting aviation may like to contribute to the proposed memorial near the spot where he fell.
>
> Subscriptions should be sent to the Pilcher Memorial Fund, Messrs. Barclay and Co. (Gosling Branch), 19, Fleet Street, EC.
>
> *Braye*
> *Frank Hedges Butler.*

(The late P. S. Pilcher, who carried on the work begun by Lilienthal, was a member of the Aeronautical Society, and at the time of his death a Member of the Council.—EDS)

At a meeting of the ASGB at the Royal United Service Institution, Whitehall, on December 18, 1911, Major-General Ruck opened the proceedings with an announcement concerning the subscription to the memorial:

> Lord Braye is very anxious to erect a memorial on the spot where he died, but the subscription list at the present time falls short by £25 of the amount required. The Council of the Society, considering the prominent part which Pilcher took in the affairs of the Society, would very gladly have provided this money out of the funds of the Society, but unfortunately the present state of the funds do not admit of this, so they are constrained to ask for individual subscriptions and I am to ask those of you who wish to subscribe to send your subscriptions to the Secretary.[1]

In the January 1912 issue of the *Journal,* the Council thanked the following donors for their subscriptions:

	£	*s*	*d*
Mrs. Robinson (Percy's elder sister)	5	0	0
H. Massac Buist	5	0	0
M. Atkinson Adam	1	1	0
W. E. Gibson	1	1	0
Mervyn O'Gorman	1	1	0
Alex McCallum	0	10	0
H. F. Lloyd	0	5	0
Harry Turrill	0	5	0
John H. Ledeboer	0	5	0
T. O'Brien Hubbard	0	5	0

The Pilcher memorial in Stanford Park, Rugby, was erected in 1912. This photograph was taken on September 18, 1984. (Author)

These totaled £14 13s Od. Notable contributors are Alex McCallum, whom Pilcher assisted in his preparation of the paper "The Navigation of the Air," Mervyn O'Gorman, superintendent of the Army Aircraft Factory at Farnborough, and J. H. Ledeboer and T. O'Brien Hubbard, who had edited and prefaced a reprint of Pilcher's 1897 Dublin lecture as one of the society's *Aeronautical Classics,* published in 1910.

Further subscriptions were announced in the next issue of the *Journal:*

	£	*s*	*d*
Mrs. Tidswell (Ella)	2	0	0
C.H.M.A. Alderson	1	1	0
Major B. Baden-Powell	1	1	0
Griffith Brewer	1	1	0
Alex Ogilvie	1	1	0
Col. H. E. Rawson	0	10	0

	£	s	d
Col. F. G. Stone	0	10	0
W. H. A.	0	5	0
A. E. Berriman	0	5	0
C. C. Turner	0	5	0

These contributions brought the total to £22 12s 0d, and the society announced that the fund was now closed and a check was being forwarded to Lord Braye. "The work of erecting the memorial column at Stanford Park has been commenced," reported the *Journal,* "and it is hoped that the unveiling will take place in June."

The column still stands today. Its plinth bears two inscriptions: on one side "Percy Pilcher, pioneer of aviation, fell here, September 30, 1899," and on the other the Latin phrase "Icaro Alteri," which, translated, reads "Another Icarus." The field in which it stands, originally called "Hall Field," is now known as "Memorial Field."

Appendix E

Reproduction Pilcher Gliders

Of the five different gliders built by Pilcher, only the Hawk, his best known, has been the subject of reproductions. No fewer than six were built at the time of writing.

The first reproduction was built in 1930 for the Science Museum, London, by Martin and Millar, engineers of Norton Park, Edinburgh. Costing £100, it was delivered to the museum on December 24, 1930, when it was "weighed in" at 52 pounds.[1] It has been on display since then (the fabric, as in all but one of the reproductions, is attached beneath, rather than above, the ribs), and is currently exhibited in the Aeronautics Gallery. It is No. 57 in the British Aircraft Preservation Council's register.

The second reproduction was built by apprentices of Armstrong Whitworth Aircraft, Coventry, in 1957–58, under the supervision of Alan Jenkin.[2] After completion it was presented to Lord Braye by the Royal Aeronautical Society on March 26, 1958, for display in the newly established Pilcher Museum in his home, Stanford Hall, close by the site of Pilcher's fatal accident.[3] This glider is BAPC No. 45. In 1980 British Aerospace apprentices from Bitteswell went to Stanford Hall and renewed the glider's rigging wires under the supervision of Special Project Engineer Dick Eales. The original rigging wires were of soft iron locking wire, and had rusted in the damp atmosphere of the converted stable where the machine hangs. They were replaced by stainless steel wire, and the glider was given a general cleanup. Unfortunately, its tail boom, which has warped badly, was not replaced.[4]

The third Hawk reproduction appeared in 1959. It was built in Berkshire by "glider doctor" Don Campbell for the aforementioned BBC television program about the missing Pilcher engine. It was not a close copy, and its undercarriage was not sprung, but the fabric was correctly attached to the tops of the wings. On July 18, 1959, it was tested three times by Walter Neumark of the Derbyshire and Lancashire Gliding Club in the grounds of Stanford Hall, but was damaged in a heavy landing on the last attempt. Launch was by a Pfeifer winch loaned by the RAF Gliding Club. According to Neumark, this copy, which was exceedingly tail-heavy, weighed 80 pounds.[5] If that is correct, it was 30 pounds overweight. The cause of the accident seems to have been that the center of gravity was too far aft. As a result of the mishap, no film of the reproduction was used on the BBC program. By December 1959 Campbell had repaired the glider, and it was advertised for sale "in first class order" as "the only flying replica of the Percy Pilcher 'Hawk' in existence."[6] The machine's subsequent history is obscure. Rumors that it was stored in the roof of Personal Plane Services' hangar at Wycombe Air Park, Bucks, as BAPC No. 103 proved unfounded. (This machine is a wire-braced biplane hang glider à la Chanute.)

As a contribution to the Centenary of the Royal Aeronautical Society in 1966, No. 2175 (Rolls-Royce) Squadron, Air Training Corps, at Hillington, near Glasgow, built the fourth Hawk reproduction. It is displayed in the Museum of Transport, Pollokshields, Glasgow. Unfortunately, its fin is misproportioned, being much too tall. This glider is BAPC No. 48.

The fifth Hawk reproduction was built for a film project by Charles Paton in 1972, while he was a student at the Central School of Art, Southampton Row, London. Flight tests met with very little success, but a one-third-scale model was built to fly beneath free balloons. The cord whipping on the fuselage frame was strengthened with glass fiber. Charles eventually moved his Hawk to his workshop in East London, where it is stored. It received the BAPC No. 131 in 1979.[7]

Construction of the last Hawk reproduction to be built, no. 6, was instigated by Alex Gourlay of the BBC's props department in Glasgow. It was built to appear in BBC Scotland's television serial *King's Royal,* and was the work of Tom Abernethy of Gartmore, Stirling. Costing "around £1,200," it took six weeks to construct. An "exact replica," it uses the "proper original materials and con-

The second Hawk reproduction to be built, the work of Armstrong Whitworth apprentices at Coventry in 1958, went into the newly established Pilcher Museum in Stanford Hall, Rugby. This photograph shows it shortly after completion. (British Aerospace)

The sixth and most recent Hawk reproduction was this one, built by Tom Abernethy of Stirling in 1982 for the BBC Scotland television serial "King's Royal." (BBC Scotland)

struction details.'' Alex Gourlay reported that ''in attempting to fly the glider we only managed a few short hops, and since that gave us enough for our filming requirements we did not try again for fear of damaging the machine.'' ''More ambitious flying sequences'' were simulated with a one-sixth-scale model. In late 1982 this Hawk was allocated the registration BAPC 170 in Mr. Gourlay's name.[8]

Appendix F

The Cardross and Eynsford Sites Today

Visit to Cardross, Dumbartonshire, Scotland, June 25, 1984

Don Storer of the Royal Museum of Scotland, Edinburgh, drove me across to Cardross on the north bank of the Firth of Clyde, and we proceeded to Wallacetown Farm, where, it is recorded, Pilcher conducted his first flight trials (earliest reference to the site is in *The American Engineer and Railroad Journal* for August 1895, p. 387). However, a comparison of the farm buildings with those seen in contemporary photographs of the Beetle and Bat (third form) quickly revealed that this was not the site at which the pictures were taken.

The owner of the farm suggested that we try Walton Farm, a short distance to the southeast, and at first we thought that this was, indeed, the place we sought. Closer examination proved that we were again off target, but the owner stated that the farmhouse at Auchensail, to the north of Cardross, resembled the one in the photographs. This struck a chord with me, as I recalled a short article in the *Helensburgh and Gareloch Times* for October 2, 1895, which began with the words "Some interesting experiments are being carried out quietly at Auchinsail [*sic*] in the parish of Cardross with a new flying machine."

As we were driving northward to Auchensail I recognized a road junction from a photograph in the Pilcher album in my possession. It turned out to be the junction at St. Mahew's Chapel. The scenery is little changed from 1895, the same buildings and the distinctive stone gateposts being conspicuous.

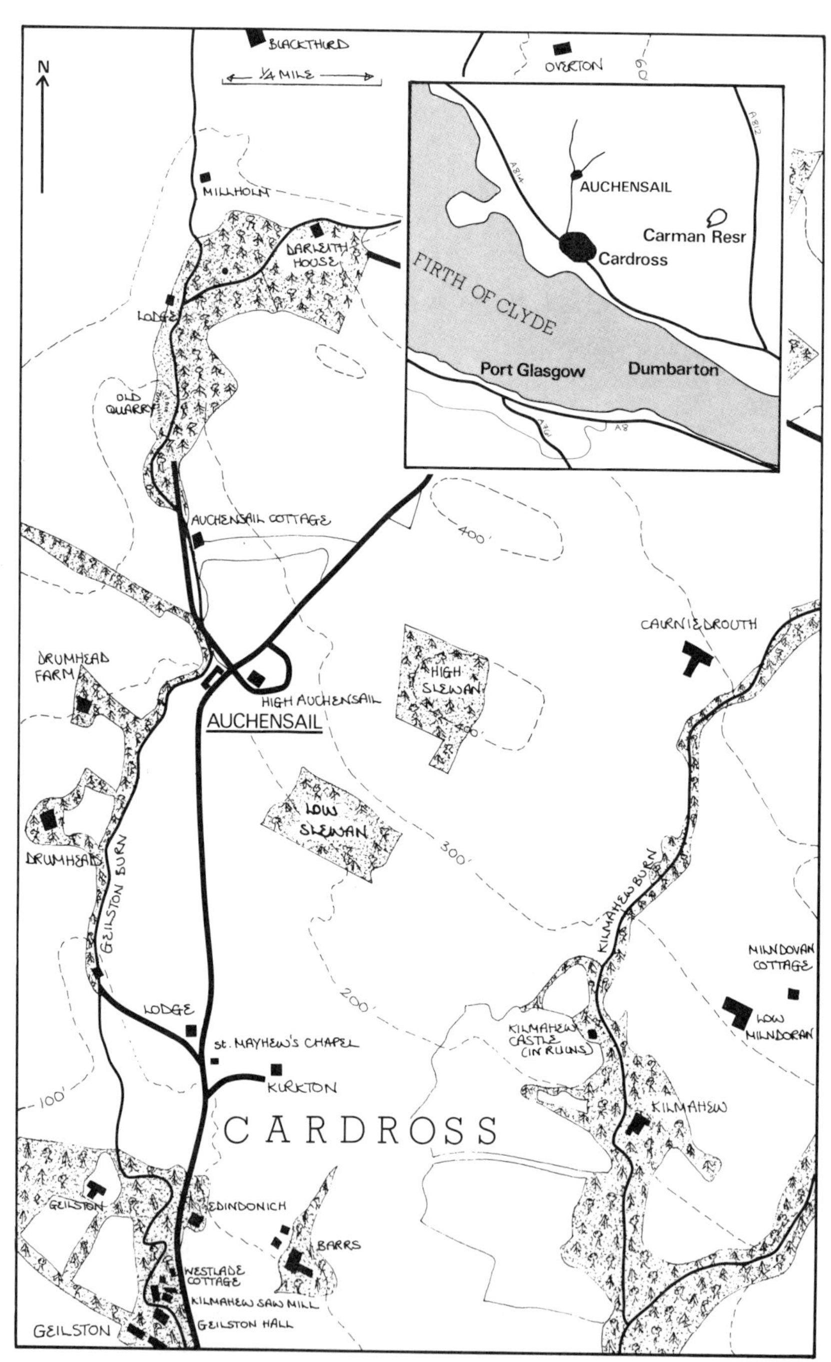

Map of Cardross area, based on an 1899 Ordnance Survey map.

As we approached Auchensail (now locally known as Low Auchensail, to distinguish it from nearby High Auchensail), it was obvious that this was the farm depicted in the photographs. The farmhouse itself, which faces approximately southwest, has barely changed at all, even the chimney pots being recognizable. Set sideways to the house and extending behind it is a long barn. Until a few years ago this barn turned a right angle at the end furthest from the house (shown on the 1899 Ordnance Survey Map, Dumbartonshire, Sheet XVII SE), but this right-angled section was destroyed by fire. The corner of this right angle and the destroyed "leg" are shown in pictures of Ella Pilcher with two other ladies on the site in 1895, and of the Bat (third form) outside the barn.

Ella wrote, "We took a farmhouse with a very large, empty barn at Cardross," and it seems probable that this is the place referred to. What seems to be the case is that Pilcher made his first trials with the Bat at Wallacetown Farm, then moved to Auchensail, where he built the Beetle in the barn (it was not as easily demountable as the Bat), and modified the Bat. The Auchensail site is clearly much more sheltered than the area near Wallacetown, where the hills are exposed. This suggests that he would have found the site more suitable for preliminary trials, especially in view of the Beetle's large expanse of wing.

The map reference for Auchensail is lat. 34° 25′ N long. 79° 50′ W. The farm's present owner is Alan McCandlish, who recalls being told that flights were made from a hill called Killoeter. This seems extremely doubtful, as this hill is very steep and quite a distance from the farm.

Visit to Upper Austin Lodge Farm, Eynsford, Kent, September 19, 1981

When I first arrived, Richard Tustian, the farm manager, informed me that the site of Maxim's hangar was thought to be on the west side of the road leading to the farmhouse and north of the main buildings, as indicated on the farm map. However, after spending some time reconnoitering the surrounding fields to determine the points from which the period pictures could have been taken, I was not convinced that I could locate any of them in that area.

The farmhouse at Auchensail as it now appears. Compare with the photograph on p. 20. (Author)

Upon returning to the farmhouse I met Harry Gadd, the farm foreman, who has worked there since 1953. When shown the pictures, Harry quickly pinpointed all of the sites as areas to the south of the farmhouse, and subsequently we were able to locate them and determine the approximate positions from which the pictures were taken.

The details are as follows: The picture on page 61 showing Pilcher with the Hawk outside Maxim's hangar in 1896, when the glider had no fin, was taken looking north-northwest (see 'A' on map).

The hangar was sited as indicated on the map, where the northern ends of two chicken broiler houses now stand. There are no remains. However, an open-fronted shed in the background of another picture taken at the time still stands, and is used as a garage. A small group of trees across the curved path from the shed in this picture are now fully grown horse chestnuts, and trees also obscure the background hills.

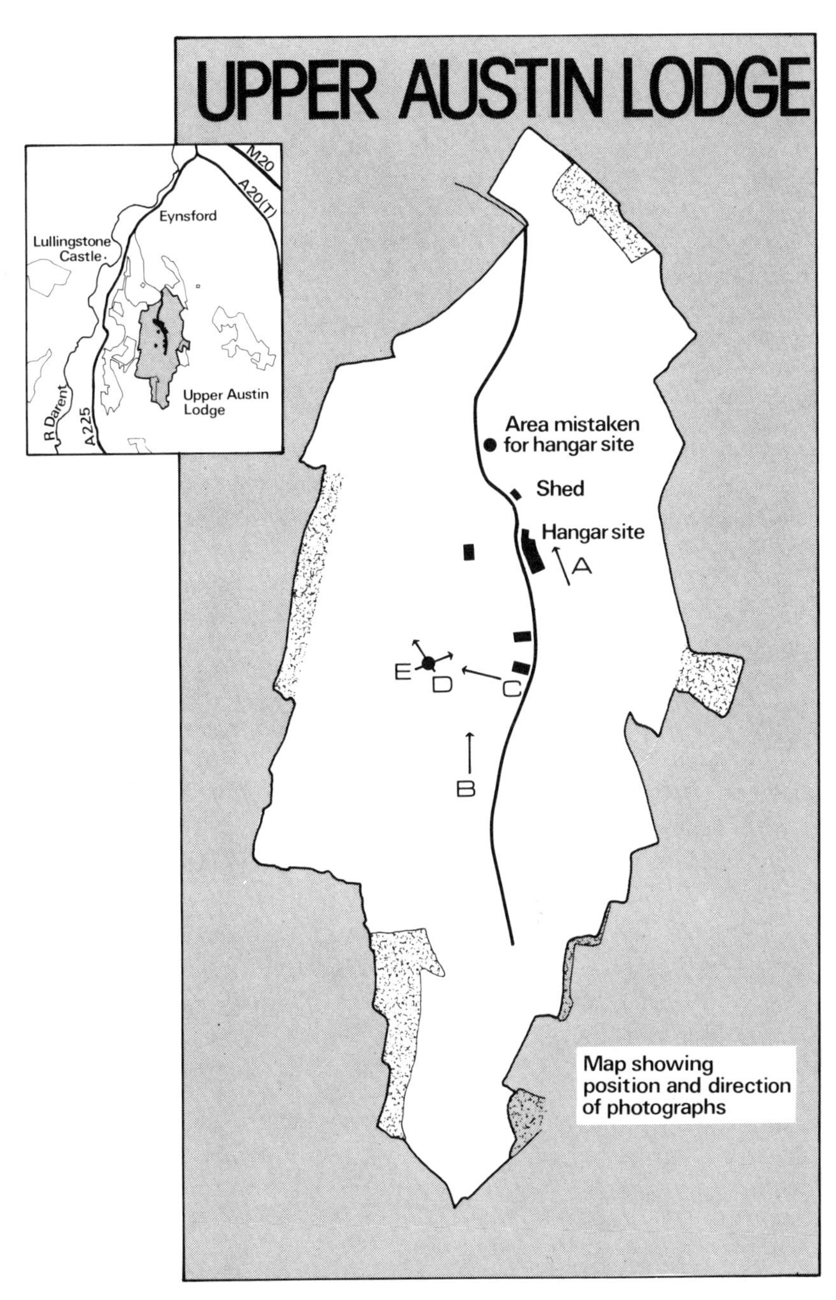

Map of Upper Austin Lodge.

The bottom picture on page 78 showing Pilcher gliding under tow in the Hawk at Eynsford in 1897 (see 'B' on map) was taken looking in a northerly direction, as indicated by the position of Maxim's hangar at the extreme right of the picture. The field in which the picture was taken rises in a north-northwesterly direction to "the Knob," the highest point on the farm, which is about 500 feet above sea level. A hedgerow cuts off the field from the Knob, as it did in Pilcher's time.

The top picture of Pilcher under tow in the Hawk in 1897 on page 78 shows him gliding from the same field as in the other picture, but was taken looking west-northwest, with the Knob clearly seen rising behind the hedgerow (see 'C' on map). Although the Knob is still grass-covered, the lower field is now cultivated.

The picture on page 77 showing Pilcher posing in the Hawk in 1897 was taken right on top of the Knob, with the camera pointing approximately northwest (see 'D' on map). The other picture on page 77, was taken from this point, looking approximately east-northeast ('E' on map). It seems possible that Pilcher took off from the Knob under tow and passed over the hedgerow and across the lower field.

At the time the pictures were taken the area was used by the Maxim and Nordenfeld Company as a testing range for automatic and quick-firing guns. Hence Maxim's ability to have his hangar on the land. As the 1910 Ordnance Survey map shows, the "Eynsford Range" extended right down the west side of Upper Austin Lodge Farm, on the other side of the Knob to the scene of the gliding flights.

It is quite possible that other fields were used, according to wind direction at the time of trials. A large field adjacent to the Farm on the east side, directly east of the hangar site, is still known as the "Flying Field," but whether there is any sound factual basis behind this name is unknown.

Notes

Chapter 1: To Breast the Breeze, 1867–95

1. See H. C. Levis, *The British King Who Tried to Fly* (London: Chiswick Press, 1919; reprinted as *Bladud of Bath,* Bath: West Country Editions, 1973); R. J. Stewart, *The Myth of Bladud,* (Bath City Council, 1980); R. J. Stewart, *The Waters of the Gap,* (Bath City Council, 1981).
2. The information in this paragraph is taken from Pilcher's birth certificate (General Register Office, London).
3. Sir Gonne Pilcher, "Note on the Pilcher Family," November 1963, plus other family records. Copy in the author's files.
4. Will of Thomas Webb Pilcher, General Register Office, London.
5. Pilcher, "Note on the Pilcher Family."
6. E. Tidswell (née Pilcher), "The Work and Experiments of Percy S. Pilcher," *Aeronautical Journal,* July 1909, p. 87.
7. Ibid.
8. Details of Pilcher's cadet records were supplied by Britannia Royal Naval College, Dartmouth, Devon.
9. Information on Pilcher's naval career is from his discharge forms and midshipman's logbook for the period 2 September 1882, to 10 February 1884, now in the author's possession, and from another logbook held by the Lord Braye at Stanford Hall, Rugby. Both logbooks are incomplete.
10. Details of the various ships on which Pilcher served are from J. J. Colledge, *Ships of the Royal Navy: An Historical Index,* vol. 1 (Newton Abbott: David and Charles, 1969).
11. Ibid.
12. Cadet records, Britannia Royal Naval College.
13. Colledge, *Ships of the Royal Navy.*

14. Ibid.
15. Ibid.
16. Although it is common practice to assume one rank higher upon leaving the service, this usually applies only to the ranks of lieutenant commander and higher, though it may have applied to lieutenants at the time in question. Martin Andrewartha of the Science Museum, London, suggests that Pilcher became "lieutenant" because midshipman was not a recognized rank—although it was not a "rate" either, and the rank of lieutenant was the best way of "explaining away" seven years in the Royal Navy.
17. Lord Braye in conversation with the author, 15 May 1979.
18. P. S. Pilcher, Institution of Naval Architects, Form of Proposal of Associate, 1892. Pilcher lists his career briefly and gives his address as 20 Alfred Place West, London SW. In the Royal Institution of Naval Architects archives. See also I. R. Liddell, "Percy S. Pilcher," the First Pilcher Memorial Lecture, delivered before the Glasgow Branch of the Royal Aeronautical Society in the Royal Technical College, Glasgow, 10 February 1956. Typescript of corrected original draft in the Royal Aeronautical Society Library, London. Amended second draft in the Royal Scottish Museum, Edinburgh.
19. R. C. Gray, "Percy Sinclair Pilcher (1867–1899)," *College Courant* (journal of the Glasgow University Graduates Association), vol. 8, no. 15 (Martinmas 1955), p. 37.
20. See n. 18.
21. Ibid.
22. Tidswell, "Work and Experiments."
23. T. O'B. Hubbard and J. H. Ledeboer, (eds.), *The Aeronautical Classics No. 5, Gliding, by P. S. Pilcher* (Aeronautical Society of Great Britain, London, 1910), p. viii; Liddell, "Percy S. Pilcher."
24. Letter to the author from the Academic Department, University of London, 20 July 1982.
25. See n. 18.
26. In the author's possession.
27. See n. 18. Liddell, "Percy S. Pilcher," and Gray, "Percy Sinclair Pilcher," both state that he took up this post in 1892, but I have followed Percy's own dates here.
28. E. Tidswell to J. E. Hodgson, 20 May 1935, Envelope 14, C. H. Bookcase, RAeS Library. Percy was a member of the Institute of Naval Architects, and in a letter to Hodgson dated January 27, 1929, Ella wrote: "I always used to go to the outings of the Institute of Naval Architects with my brother." In the Institute's Transactions there are several instances recorded of Pilcher contributing to discussions after lectures. In 1895, for example, following a lecture on the "Evaporative Efficiency of Water-tube Boilers," he drew the members' attention to the boiler that Maxim had used in his flying machine. In 1896, he proposed three designs of watertight doors for ships and in 1899 he spoke on brazing materials during a lecture discussion.

The Royal Aeronautical Society library holds a notebook of "Odd Notes" dated 1891–93 that relates to ship design. Apart from notes by Pilcher at the front of the book, it contains mainly clippings, chiefly from the *Engineer.*

29. "Pilcher's Soaring Machine," *American Engineer and Railroad Journal,* August 1895, p. 387.
30. S. Mavor, "Memories No. 4. A Pioneer of Flight," *M & C Apprentices' Magazine,* Summer 1934, p. 57.
31. From undated, handwritten notes by Thora Forrester, Pilcher's niece.
32. Mavor, "Memories."
33. Ibid.
34. R. C. Gray, "Scotland's First Airman," *Glasgow Herald,* 1 February 1937.
35. P. S. Pilcher, "Matchbox Holder," British Patent No. 20,767, 2 November 1893, and P. S. Pilcher, "Covers for Glasses, Cups &c," British Patent No. 20,768, 2 November (London: Patent Office, 1893).
36. A typescript of Provisional Specification No. 15,614 survives in the Pilcher papers, Envelope 14, C. H. Bookcase, RAeS Library.
37. In London Patent Office records.
38. Gray, "Scotland's First Airman."
39. For full details of Lilienthal's work, see E. Schwipps, *Lilienthal* (Berlin: Arani-Verlag GmbH, 1979 & 1986); G. Halle, *Otto Lilienthal* (Düsseldorf: VDI-Verlag GmbH, 1976); and G. Halle, *Otto Lilienthal und seine Flugzeug-Konstruktionen,* Deutsches Museum abhandlungen und berichte, vol. 30, no. 2 (1962). Also see C. H. Gibbs-Smith, *Aviation* (London: Her Majesty's Stationery Office, 1970 & 1985).
40. P. S. Pilcher, "Soaring Machine," *Aeronautical Journal,* January 1898, p. 7.
41. Gray, "Scotland's First Airman."
42. See Gray, "Percy Sinclair Pilcher," p. 42; and Liddell, "Percy S. Pilcher."
43. P. S. Pilcher, *Experiments in Flying Machines,* paper read before the Military Society of Ireland, 21 January 1897 (Dublin: Dollard, 1897), p. 9.
44. "Aerial Navigation. Flying Machines; Experiments at Cardross," *Glasgow Evening Citizen,* 19 October 1895, p. 3.
45. Tidswell, "Work and Experiments," p. 87.
46. "Aerial Navigation," *Glasgow Evening Citizen,* 19 October 1985.
47. "Pilcher's Soaring Machine," *American Engineer and Railroad Journal,* August 1895, p. 387. As Octave Chanute contributed the aeronautical items to the *American Engineer and Railroad Journal,* this article would seem to point to the earliest contact between Pilcher and Chanute. However, even in Chanute's meticulously kept letter files there is no correspondence with Pilcher at this early date. A few details of the cost of materials have survived. The Royal Aeronautical Society's display at the International Aero Exhibition, Olympia, London, July 16–27, 1929, included some Pilcher items lent by Ella Tidswell, among them "Manuscript notes on the

'Bat,' with account of expenditure on materials, *e.g.* Sail material, 12/-; Wood for panelwork, 10/-; Pins, Tape, etc., 3/7; Tacks 3½d. Also a specimen of the fabric used for the wings." Sadly, these items do not seem to have survived, but the foregoing details were recorded in a list of exhibits published in the *Aeronautical Journal,* October 1929, p. 996.

48. Ella is said to have sewn the wings and helped generally with all of Pilcher's gliders, later assisted by Professor Biles's daughter Iris, later Lady Chalmers; see Gray, "Percy Sinclair Pilcher."
49. The graphic phrase is Ella's; see Tidswell, "Work and Experiments." The general description has been compiled mainly from the information in n. 47 and from "Pilcher's Soaring Apparatus," *Practical Engineer,* 6 December 1895, p. 484.
50. Tidswell, "Work and Experiments."
51. Pilcher, *Experiments in Flying Machines,* p. 11.
52. P. S. Pilcher, "Experiments with Soaring Machines," *Nature,* 20 February 1896, p. 365.
53. P. S. Pilcher, Paper to Students Engineering Society, Glasgow, 12 December 1895. Original lecture notes, RAeS Library, p. 15.
54. The word "cave" is Pilcher's, from his 1897 Dublin lecture; see n. 43, p. 7.
55. Pilcher, *Experiments in Flying Machines,* p. 6.
56. O. Lilienthal, *Der Vogelflug als Grundlage der Fliegekunst,* (Berlin: R. Gaertners Verlag, 1889).
57. O. Chanute, *Progress in Flying Machines* (New York: American Engineer and Railroad Journal, 1894), p. 201.
58. Ibid. p. 207.
59. Pilcher, paper to Students Engineering Society, Glasgow, p. 7.
60. Chanute, *Progress,* p. 279.
61. H. F. Phillips, "Blades for Deflecting Air," British Patent No. 13,768 (London: Patent Office, 1884).
62. F. W. Lanchester, *Aerodynamics,* (London: Constable, 1907), p. 141.
63. Ibid., p. 142.
64. H. W. L. Moedebeck, *Pocket-book of Aeronautics,* (London: Whittaker, 1907), pp. 287–88.
65. Pilcher, *Experiments in Flying Machines,* p. 5.
66. Ibid., p. 10.
67. "Pilcher's Soaring Machine."
68. "Pilcher's Soaring Apparatus," p. 484.
69. Pilcher, *Experiments in Flying Machines,* p. 10.
70. "Pilcher's Soaring Apparatus," pp. 484–85.
71. Ibid., p. 485.
72. "Pilcher's Soaring Machine."

73. Pilcher, *Experiments in Flying Machines,* p. 12.
74. P. S. Pilcher to L. Hargrave, 25 June 1896, Hargrave Papers, RAeS Library.
75. Tidswell, "Work and Experiments," p. 88. Clipping from *Helensburgh and Gareloch Times,* 2 October 1895, Pilcher's Scrapbook No. 1, p. 36, RAeS Library. See appendix F. Records in the Scottish Record Office reveal that in 1895 the farm of Auchensail was owned by John William Burns of Kilmahew and tenanted by James Colquhoun, farmer.
76. "Pilcher's Flying Machine," *American Engineer and Railroad Journal,* 1 November 1895, p. 490.
77. Ibid.
78. Pilcher, *Experiments in Flying Machines*, p. 12.
79. "Pilcher's Soaring Apparatus," p. 485.
80. "Pilcher's Flying Machine."
81. "Pilcher's Soaring Apparatus," p. 485.
82. Tidswell, "Work and Experiments," p. 88.
83. Pilcher, *Experiments in Flying Machines,* p. 13.
84. "Pilcher's Flying Machine."
85. Pilcher, "Experiments with Soaring Machines," pp. 365–66.
86. "Pilcher's Soaring Apparatus," p. 485.
87. Tidswell, "Work and Experiments," p. 88.
88. "Pilcher's Soaring Apparatus," p. 485.
89. Ibid.
90. Pilcher, "Experiments with Soaring Machines," p. 365.
91. Pilcher, paper to Students' Engineering Society, Glasgow, p. 20.
92. Original annotated drawing in the C. H. Bookcase, RAeS Library.
93. See Lilienthal references, n. 39.
94. Pilcher, paper to Students' Engineering Society, Glasgow, p. 8.
95. Pilcher, *Experiments in Flying Machines,* p. 14.
96. Gray, "Percy Sinclair Pilcher," p. 40.
97. Pilcher, paper to Students' Engineering Society, Glasgow, p. 25.
98. W. Raleigh, *The War in the Air,* vol. 1 (Oxford: Clarendon Press, 1922), p. 49. Also reported in the *Glasgow Herald,* 25 November 1909, in a report on the first public meeting of the Scottish Aeronautical Society, at which Biles gave a short address.
99. S. Mavor, "Memories," p. 60.
100. Quoted in Gibbs-Smith, *Aviation,* p. 92.
101. P. S. Pilcher, RAeS Library.
102. Original drawing in RAeS Library.
103. Pilcher, lecture to Students' Engineering Society, Glasgow. On p. 25 he says of the new machine, "meant to have had it here."

104. This quotation and the following details of Pilcher's lecture come from his own notes, paper to the Students' Engineering Society, Glasgow, now in the RAeS Library.

105. None of the Pilcher-Lilienthal correspondence is known to survive, but in his lecture to the students Pilcher refers to letters from Lilienthal, and his scrapbook No. 1 in the RAeS Library contains a copy of a reprint of "Die Profile der Segelflächen und ihre Wirkung" by Otto Lilienthal, from *Zeitschrift für Luftschiffart und Physik der Atmosphäre,* February-March 1895. On it, Pilcher has written, "Sent by Herr Lilienthal about July '95."

106. See S. P. Langley, *Experiments in Aerodynamics* (Washington, D.C.: Smithsonian Institution, 1891).

107. See T. D. Crouch, *A Dream of Wings,* (New York: W. W. Norton, 1981), chap. 7.

108. Sir H. S. Maxim, *Artificial and Natural Flight* (London: Whittaker, 1908); Sir H. S. Maxim, *My Life,* (London: Methuen, 1915), chap. 26.

109. Quotations are from an undated and unidentified newspaper clipping of a report of the lecture, Pilcher's scrapbook No. 1, RAeS Library. The newspaper is Scottish and was published shortly after the lecture date.

110. "The Pennington Engine," *Autocar,* 16 November 1895, pp. 28–30; "More about the Pennington Motor," *Autocar,* 7 December 1895, pp. 63–66. The latter article included a general working drawing: "the first time in any printed publication," boasted *Autocar.*

111. Undated clipping from the *Practical Engineer,* Pilcher's scrapbook no. 1, RAeS Library.

Chapter 2: Pastures New, 1896

1. For a full account of Hargrave's work, see W. H. Shaw and O. Ruhen, *Lawrence Hargrave—Explorer, Inventor, and Aviation Experimenter* (New South Wales and Melbourne: Cassell Australia, 1977).
2. L. Hargrave to P. S. Pilcher, 11 December 1895, Folder 4, RAeS Library.
3. "The Lilienthal and Pilcher Gliders Compared," *Flight,* 8 January 1910, p. 21.
4. "Lilienthal's Experiments on Flying," *Nature,* 30 January 1896, p. 301.
5. P. S. Pilcher, "Experiments with Soaring Machines," *Nature,* 20 February 1896, p. 366.
6. Hargrave to Pilcher, 24 April 1896, Hargrave Papers, RAeS Library. Hargrave says, "the Glasgow paper did not turn up."
7. P. S. Pilcher to L. Hargrave, 16 March 1896, Hargrave Papers, RAeS Library.
8. P. S. Pilcher, *Experiments in Flying Machines,* paper read before the Military Society of Ireland, 21 January 1897 (Dublin: Dollard, 1897). On p. 14 he says, "In this machine [the Hawk] I have done away with the vertical rudder [fin] altogether. Whether this is an advantage or not I am not certain."

9. P. S. Pilcher, "Improvements in Flying and Soaring Machines," British Patent No. 9144, 1896, London: Patent Office. Much of the foregoing description is from this source, as well as from "Lilienthal and Pilcher Gliders Compared."
10. P. S. Pilcher, "Soaring Machine," *Aeronautical Journal,* January 1898, p. 7.
11. P. S. Pilcher and H. S. Maxim, "Imperial Institute Exhibition of Motors," Maxim technical file, Science Museum.
12. Pilcher wrote to Hargrave from Glasgow University on March 16, but a drawing made on April 19 was made with an exhibition at London's Imperial Institute in mind, so he must have moved to London between these dates.
13. Details of the Maxim and Nordenfeld Company are from J. D. Scott, *Vickers, a History* (London: Weidenfeld and Nicolson, 1962); and C. Trebilcock, *The Vickers Brothers* (London: Europa Publications, 1977).
14. H. S. Maxim, *My Life* (London: Methuen, 1915), pp. 294, 297.
15. The quotation is from Trebilcock, *Vickers Brothers,* p. 37.
16. The histories of the gliders that survived Pilcher will be found in the Postscript.
17. P. S. Pilcher, drawing of "Proposed Lifting Platform," 19 April 1896, C. H. Bookcase, RAeS Library.
18. *Autocar,* 2 May 1896, p. 316 (letter from Frederick R. Simms, Vice-President of the Motor Car Club; *Imperial Institute Journal,* March 1896, page 94, "International Exhibition of Motors and Their Appliances."
19. "Summer Season Exhibition, 1896," *Imperial Institute Journal,* June 1896, p. 205.
20. "International Horseless Carriage Exhibition at the Imperial Institute," *Autocar*, 16 May 1896, p. 344.
21. Letter from Frederick R. Simms.
22. "International Exhibition of Motors and Their Appliances," *Imperial Institute Journal,* April 1896, p. 128.
23. Pilcher and Maxim, *Imperial Institute Exhibition of Motors;* "International . . .," *Autocar* 16 May 1896.
24. "International . . . ," *Autocar*, 16 May 1896.
25. Pilcher and Maxim, "Imperial Institute Exhibition."
26. P. S. Pilcher, "Gliding Experiments," in *The Aeronautical Annual,* ed. J. Means (Boston: W. B. Clarke & Co., 1897), p. 146.
27. Pilcher, *Experiments in Flying Machines,* p. 8.
28. Pilcher, "Gliding Experiments," p. 146.
29. Pilcher, *Experiments in Flying Machines,* p. 8.
30. Hargrave to Pilcher, 24 April 1896, Hargrave Papers.
31. Pilcher to Hargrave, 25 June 1896, Hargrave Papers.
32. H. S. Maxim, "Improvements in Aerial or Flying Machines," British Patent No. 10,620, 1897, London: Patent Office.

33. T. D. Crouch, *A Dream of Wings* (New York: W. W. Norton, 1981), p. 152.
34. Shaw and Ruhen, *Lawrence Hargrave.*
35. "The Imperial Institute Exhibition," *Autocar,* 25 July 1896, p. 464.
36. C. H. Gibbs-Smith, *Aviation* (London: Her Majesty's Stationery Office, 1970), p. 79.
37. D. Archibald, "The Possibility of Human Flight," *Saturday Review,* 22 August 1896, p. 181–82.
38. Shaw and Ruhen, *Lawrence Hargrave,* p. 84.
39. P. S. Pilcher, "The Possibility of Human Flight," *Saturday Review,* 5 September 1896.
40. Gibbs-Smith, *Aviation,* p. 79.
41. See G. Halle, *Otto Lilienthal* (Düsseldorf: VDI-Verlag, 1976), p. 162; and W. Schwipps, *Lilienthal* (Berlin: Arani-Verlag, 1979), p. 385.
42. Archibald, "Possibility of Human Flight," *Saturday Review,* 12 September 1896, pp. 287–88.
43. W. E. G. Fisher, "Flying Men," *Glasgow Herald,* 22 August 1896.
44. Pilcher, *Experiments in Flying Machines,* p. 14.
45. Ibid.
46. P. S. Pilcher to unknown, 24 November 1896. Letter in the author's possession.
47. It appears that Pilcher used the same notes for this lecture as for the Dublin lecture given a week earlier.
48. "Flying Machines. The Maxim-Pilchar [*sic*] Experiments. New Development Expected," *Glasgow Evening Citizen,* 29 January 1897. Clipping in Chanute's scrapbook, "Materials for the Study of the Aeronautical Experiments of Percy S. Pilcher," comp. Octave Chanute, MS. 132, Department of Special Collections, University of Chicago.
49. Pilcher, *Experiments in Flying Machines,* pp. 14–15.
50. P. S. Pilcher, scrapbook no. 4, RAeS Library, contains several clippings on this event.
51. P. S. Pilcher, untitled and undated typescript notes for a vote of thanks to Dr. Bryan, C. H. Bookcase, Envelope 14, RAeS Library.
52. E. Tidswell to J. E. Hodgson, 8 April 1925, C. H. Bookcase, Envelope 14, RAeS Library.
53. A. G. Wilson, (son of Walter Wilson), Draft of an interview with C. H. Gibbs-Smith in June 1970. Copy in author's files.
54. Ibid.
55. W. G. Wilson, "Pilcher's Gliding Experiments," paper read to the Cambridge University Engineering Society at Cambridge on 21 February 1923. Copy of paper supplied by A. G. Wilson, one of W. G. Wilson's sons.
56. Ibid.
57. In an album in the author's collection.

58. W. G. Wilson and P. S. Pilcher, "Improvements in Sails for Boats and other Vessels, and in Means for Setting, Working and Furling Same," British Patent No. 29,194 of 1896, London: Patent Office.

Chapter 3: A New Form of Locomotion, 1897

1. Baden-Powell wrote to Ella Pilcher from this address on 8 March 1897 concerning illustrations used in the lecture. Letter in the possession of David Forrester, son of Percy's niece, Thora.
2. Sir Gonne Pilcher, "Notes on the Pilcher Family," November 1963 (copy of MS in the author's files), states that his father—Percy's brother Thomas—"had a staff job for 2 to 3 years in Dublin in the middle 'nineties.' . . . In about 1898 he was sent to Nigeria." Thomas himself had dabbled in the aeronautic arts about 1894 when, as a captain in the Northumberland Fusiliers, he had made some manlifting kite trials. Baden-Powell wrote in the *Aeronautical Journal* for April 1897 that "Capt. Pilcher . . . made some trials with a number of canvas discs attached to the string of a small kite, and by this means was more than once lifted off his legs." It is not known whether these tentative experiments influenced or inspired Percy in any way.
3. "Aerial Machines Lecture before the Military Society," *Freeman's Journal,* (Dublin), 22 January 1897. Clipping in Chanute's Pilcher scrapbook, Crerar MS. 132, Department of Special Collections, University of Chicago (hereafter cited as Crerar MS. 132).
4. Published as *Experiments in Flying Machines* (Dublin: Dollard 1897). Unless otherwise stated, quotations from the lecture are from this source.
5. "Aerial Machines Lecture," *Freeman's Journal.*
6. The quotation about the model gliders is from the "Aerial Machines Lecture," *Freeman's Journal.* That on his position in the glider is from *Experiments in Flying Machines,* p. 14.
7. P. S. Pilcher, MS notes for lecture before Military Society of Ireland, Dublin, 21 January 1897, C.H. Bookcase, Envelope 14, RAeS Library, (hereafter cited as RAeS Library).
8. P. Jarrett, "Fitzgerald the Flightless," *Aeroplane Monthly,* October 1977, pp. 545–47.
9. Pilcher, notes for Dublin lecture.
10. "Flying Machines. The Maxim-Pilchar [*sic*] Experiments. New Development Expected," *Glasgow Evening Citizen,* 29 January 1897. Clipping in Chanute's Pilcher scrapbook, Crerar MS. 132.
11. "Notices of the Aeronautical Society," *Aeronautical Journal,* April 1897, p. 1.
12. P. S. Pilcher to B. F. S. Baden-Powell, RAeS Library.
13. "Mr. Pilcher on Flying Machines." *Aeronautical Journal,* April 1897, pp. 1–4.
14. See n. 12.

15. P. S. Pilcher, "Gliding Experiments," in *Aeronautical Annual 1897,* ed. J. Means (Boston, Mass.: W. B. Clarke & Co., 1897), p. 145.
16. *Western Mercury* (Plymouth), 12 June 1897. Clipping in Chanute's Pilcher scrapbook, Crerar MS. 132.
17. D. Archibald, "A New Experiment in Soaring Flight," *Pall Mall Gazette,* London, 29 June 1897. Clipping in Chanute's Pilcher scrapbook, Crerar MS. 132.
18. See chap. 2, n. 9.
19. Lt. Col. W. S. Pilcher to C. H. Gibbs-Smith, 1 July 1959, Gibbs-Smith Papers, the Science Museum, London.
20. Telephone conversation with the author, 1983.
21. "The Sportswoman's sketch-book. Mrs. Tidswell," *Lady's Pictorial,* 13 April 1907, p. 600.
22. W. J. S. Lockyer, "Soaring Flight," *Nature,* 12 August 1897, reprint in RAeS Library.
23. See chap. 2.
24. The June 19 date appeared in G. H. Bryan, "Artificial Flight," *Science Progress,* October 1897, pp. 531–53, but as the date of the "bush flight" is completely wrong in this reference, I treat it with suspicion.
25. "Pilcher's Soaring Machine," *Aeronautical Journal,* July 1897, p. 17.
26. Smithsonian Institution National Air and Space Museum, Washington, D.C., photograph negative No. A18261. Page 77 in this book.
27. "A Novelty in Sails," *Illustrated London News,* 7 August 1897, p. 192.
28. P. S. Pilcher, "Cyclone Sail," *Nature,* 12 August 1897, p. 342.
29. W. G. Wilson, "Pilcher's Gliding Experiments," paper read to the Cambridge University Engineering Society at Cambridge on February 21st, 1923, copy in the author's files.
30. "A Novelty . . .," *Illustrated London News,* 7 August 1897.
31. The drawing is recorded in an undated list of Pilcher material in Ella's possession, compiled by J.E. Hodgson about 1926. This list is now in C.H. Bookcase, Envelope 14, RAeS Library.
32. Wilson, paper on Pilcher's Gliding Experiments.
33. A. G. Wilson, (son of Walter Wilson), draft of an interview with C. H. Gibbs-Smith in June 1970, copy in author's files.
34. McCallum later became the aeronautical correspondent of the *Glasgow Herald,* and clippings of his articles for that newspaper are now held in the RAeS Library. Most of the collection, in some twenty albums, covers the period from late 1907 to May 1914; later in this period he contributed a regular weekly column entitled "Aeronautical Notes." He was elected a member of the ASGB on January 12, 1910.
35. McCallum's first letter to Pilcher, dated 10 August 1897, begins, "I hope by the end of this week to return you your newspaper cutting book."
36. A. McCallum to P. S. Pilcher, 10 August 1897, RAeS Library.

37. P. S. Pilcher to A. McCallum, 11 August 1897, RAeS Library.
38. Pilcher to McCallum, 13 August 1897, RAeS Library.
39. Pilcher to McCallum, 18 August 1897, RAeS Library.
40. A. McCallum, "The Navigation of the Air," *Glasgow Herald,* 4 September 1897, 11 September 1897, 18 September 1897, 26 September 1897.
41. Ibid., September 26.
42. An advertisement for the pamphlet appeared on the last page of the October 1897 issue of the *Aeronautical Journal.* It was published by the ASGB. In a letter to the magazine *Flight,* dated 1 February 1909 and published in the February 13 issue (pp. 96–97), McCallum says that the ASGB reprinted his articles "without any suggestion on my part."
43. The date is from the original Vickers Company minute book containing the records of the board meetings, in Vickers House, London.
44. See J. D. Scott, *Vickers. A History* (London: Weidenfeld and Nicolson, 1962), p. 45; and C. Trebilcock, *The Vickers Brothers* (London: Europa Publications, 1977), p. 38.
45. The quotation is from Scott, *Vickers. A History,* p. 45.
46. Trebilcock, *The Vickers Brothers,* p. 42.
47. O. Chanute, "Gliding Experiments," *Journal of the Western Society of Engineers,* 1897.
48. This account is compiled from Chanute's "Gliding Experiments"; and from T. Crouch, *A Dream of Wings,* (New York: W. W. Norton, 1981), chap. 9. Chanute's quotation on the Pratt truss appears on p. 605 of the former reference.
49. Crouch, *A Dream of Wings,* pp. 200–1.
50. Wilson, "Pilcher's Gliding Experiments," p. 2.
51. *Wilson and Pilcher Limited. Memorandum and Articles of Association, 1897,* Public Record Office reference BT31/7673/54767, London. Subsequent details also from this source.
52. How Calder came to be involved is obscure, but one of his sisters, Agnes, was Percy Pilcher's girlfriend. This fact came to light entirely by chance in November 1983, during a conversation with John Blake of the Society of British Aerospace Companies. John is a grandson of Agnes Calder, and remembers her describing Percy as her "beau." James Calder's address is given as Bo'ness, Scotland, which is not far from Glasgow. Whether Pilcher met James or Agnes Calder first is unknown.
53. P. S. Pilcher to B. F. S. Baden-Powell, 10 November 1897, RAeS Library.
54. *Aeronautical Journal,* October 1897, p. 1.
55. *Who Was Who, 1897–1916* (London: A. C. Black, 1920), p. 223.
56. *Aeronautical Journal,* January 1898, p. 1.
57. Pilcher to Baden-Powell, 14 November 1897, RAeS Library.
58. Pilcher to Baden-Powell, 21 November 1897, RAeS Library.

59. Wilson and Pilcher Limited, Companies Account Notice of Situation, November 22, 1897. Public Record Office reference BT31/7673/54767, London.
60. O. Chanute to P. S. Pilcher, 29 November 1897, Chanute's letterpress books, Library of Congress, Washington, D.C. As pointed out in chap. 1, n. 47, the appearance of an illustrated account of Pilcher's first experiments in the *American Engineer and Railroad Journal* for August 1895 suggests earlier direct contact between Chanute and Pilcher, as Chanute supplied aeronautical items for the *Journal.* However, Chanute's letterpress books contain no earlier letters than this one.
61. Pilcher to Baden-Powell, 8 December 1897. RAeS Library.
62. Pilcher to Baden-Powell, 12 December 1897, RAeS Library.
63. H. S. Maxim, "Flying Machines. To the Editor of The Times," *Times,* 16 June 1896, p. 16.
64. Bryan, "Artificial Flight," pp. 531–53; see also quotation in *English Mechanic and World of Science,* 24 December 1897, p. 444.
65. Bryan, "Artificial Flight," pp. 547–48.
66. T. J. Bennett to O. Chanute, 5 January 1898, Letter in Chanute Papers, Blue Box 24, Letterpress vol. 34, p. 682, Library of Congress, Washington, D.C.

Chapter 4: Transatlantic Influence, 1898

1. O. Chanute, "Some American Experiments," *Aeronautical Journal,* January 1898, pp. 9–11; also see frontispiece.
2. Ibid., pp. 9, 11, respectively.
3. P. S. Pilcher to O. Chanute, 23 January 1898, in "Materials for the Study of the Aeronautical Experiments of Percy S. Pilcher," comp. Octave Chanute, Crerar MS. 132, Department of Special Collections, University of Chicago (hereinafter cited as Crerar MS. 132). All of Pilcher's letters to Chanute come from this source.
4. O. Chanute to P. S. Pilcher, 10 February 1898, Chanute's letterpress books, Library of Congress, Washington, D.C. (hereinafter cited as Library of Congress). All of Chanute's letters to Pilcher are from this source.
5. *Wilson and Pilcher Limited. Summary of Capital and Shares.* 22 March 1898, Public Record Office reference BT31/7673/54767, London.
6. P. S. Pilcher to B. F. S. Baden-Powell, 23 March 1898, C.H. Bookcase, Envelope 14, RAeS Library (hereafter cited as RAeS Library).
7. O. Chanute, "Improvements in and relating to Flying Machines," British Patent No. 13,372 (London: Patent Office, 1897).
8. O. Chanute, "Recent Experiments in Gliding Flight," in *Aeronautical Annual,* ed. J. Means (Boston, Mass.: W. H. Clarke & Co., 1897), p. 45.

9. Chanute to Pilcher, 3 June 1898. Library of Congress.
10. T. Crouch, *A Dream of Wings,* (New York: W. W. Norton, 1981), chap. 10.
11. Pilcher to Chanute, 24 June 1898, Crerar MS. 132.
12. "Meeting of the Aeronautical Society," *Aeronautical Journal,* July 1898, pp. 51–57.
13. G. L. O. Davidson, *The Flying Machine of the Future,* August 1898, p. 2. Prospectus for Davidson's Air-Car Construction Syndicate, Limited, in the author's collection.
14. G. L. O. Davidson, "The Flying Machine of the Future," *Aeronautical Journal,* July 1898, p. 53.
15. G. L. O. Davidson, "Improvements in Flying Machines," British Patent No. 12,469 (London: Patent Office, 1896).
16. Davidson, *Flying Machine of the Future.*
17. P. M. Jarrett, "Full Marks for Trying," *Aircraft Annual '76,* (Shepperton: Ian Allan, 1975), pp. 28–36.
18. Davidson "Flying Machine of the Future," p. 54.
19. Ibid., pp. 56–57.
20. Wilson and Pilcher Limited to O. Chanute, 19 July 1898, Crerar MS. 132.
21. Crouch, *A Dream of Wings,* p. 215; and C. R. Roseberry, *Glenn Curtiss: Pioneer of Flight* (New York: Doubleday, 1972), pp. 471–72.
22. Roseberry, *Glenn Curtiss* p. 472.
23. T. Moy, O. Chanute, and A. M. Herring, "Improvements in or Relating to Means and Appliances for Effecting Aerial Navigation," British Patent No. 15,221 of 1897, London: Patent Office.
24. *Aeronautical Journal,* January 1898, pp. 6–7.
25. Chanute to Pilcher, 5 August 1898, Library of Congress.
26. Crouch, *A Dream of Wings,* chap. 10.
27. *Wilson and Pilcher Limited, Change of Situation of Registered Office, December 8, 1898,* Public Record Office reference No. BT31/7673/54767, London.
28. P. S. Pilcher to A. McCallum, 15 December 1898, RAeS Library.
29. "The Pilcher Glider," *Flight,* 5 March 1910, p. 151.
30. Original drawing in the author's possession.
31. P. S. Pilcher, undated, tinted three-view drawing of a quadruplane, RAeS Library.
32. J. E. Hodgson, "Pilcher Papers (in the possession of Mrs. Tidswell)," ca. 1926, RAeS Library.
33. E. Tidswell to J. E. Hodgson, 8 April 1925. RAeS Library.
34. Pilcher to Baden-Powell, 17 December 1898, RAeS Library.
35. Chanute's copy of the printed letter is in his Pilcher scrapbook, Crerar MS. 132.
36. Hargrave's copy of the printed letter is in the Hargrave Papers, RAeS Library.

Chapter 5: A Very Bad Business, 1899

1. O. Chanute to P. S. Pilcher, 8 January 1899, Chanute's letterpress book, Library of Congress, Washington, D.C., (hereafter cited as Library of Congress). All of Chanute's letters to Pilcher are from this source.
2. T. Crouch, *A Dream of Wings* (New York: W. W. Norton, 1981), p. 239.
3. Probably published as "Experiments in Flying, an account of the author's own inventions and adventures," *McClure's* magazine, New York, June 1900, pp. 127–33.
4. O. Chanute, "Conditions of Success in the Design of Flying Machines," *Illustrierte Aeronautische Mitteilungen,* April 1899, pp. 37–41 (transl., pp. 41–46).
5. W. G. Wilson and P. S. Pilcher, "Electric Light Brackets," British Patent No. 1100, 17 January 1899 (abandoned). London: Patent Office.
6. "Hargrave's Soaring Kites," *Aeronautical Journal,* January 1899, pp. 19–20.
7. P. S. Pilcher to B. F. S. Baden-Powell, 30 January 1899, C.H. Bookcase, Envelope 14, RAeS Library, (hereafter cited as RAeS Library).
8. P. S. Pilcher, untitled appeal for formation of syndicate, early 1899. Carbon copy of draft, RAeS Library.
9. Pilcher to Baden-Powell, 9 February 1899. RAeS Library.
10. "Fatal Aerial Machine Accident," *Rugby Advertiser,* 7 October 1899.
11. J. E. Hodgson, "Pilcher Papers (in the possession of Mrs. Tidswell)," ca. 1926, RAeS Library.
12. A. G. Wilson, draft of interview with C. H. Gibbs-Smith, June 1970. Copy in the author's files.
13. "The Wilson and Pilcher Petrol Car," *Automotor Journal,* June 1901, pp. 449–51.
14. "The 10 hp Wilson and Pilcher Car," *Autocar,* 14 March 1903, pp. 312–14; and "Petrol Cars," *Autocar,* 20 February 1904, pp. 231–32.
15. W. G. Wilson and P. S. Pilcher, British Patent No. 3941, 22 February 1899. Abandoned.
16. W. H. Shaw and O. Ruhen, *Lawrence Hargrave, Explorer, Inventor and Aviation Experimenter* (New South Wales and Melbourne: Cassell Australia, 1977), pp. 104.
17. Ibid., p. 105.
18. Ibid., p. 110.
19. W. G. Wilson and P. S. Pilcher, British Patent No. 10,589, 19 May 1899. Abandoned.
20. "The Aeronautical Society of Great Britain," *Aeronautical Journal,* July 1899, p. 49. The following account of Hargrave's lecture and the ensuing discussion are from this source, pp. 49–58.
21. Shaw and Ruhen, *Lawrence Hargrave,* p. 106.
22. "Aeronautical Society of Great Britain," p. 58.

23. Pilcher to Baden-Powell, 9 June 1899, RAeS Library.

24. P. M. Jarrett, "Dagenham Days. A History of the Aeronautical Society's Flying Ground," *Aeronautical Journal,* February 1970, pp. 134–42.

25. Pilcher to Baden-Powell, 25 July 1899, RAeS Library.

26. "Fatal . . . Accident," 7 October 1899; and "Testing a Flying Machine in Leicestershire—A Fatal Accident," *Leicestershire Daily Post,* 4 October 1899. The statement that "four successful ascents" had been made at Stanford Hall Park appears in the latter reference. The following account of the events of 30 September 1899 leans heavily on these two references.

27. "Flying Machine Accident," *Daily Telegraph,* 2 October 1899. Clipping in Chanute's Pilcher Scrapook, Crerar MS. 132.

28. Undated notes by Mr. Julian Wright in an interview with Lord Braye, 1980. In the author's files.

29. "That Fatal Flight," *Rugby Advertiser,* 27 September 1974, p. 8.

30. W. G. Wilson, "Pilcher's Gliding Experiments," paper read to the Cambridge University Engineering Society at Cambridge on 21 February 1923, p. 5. Copy of typescript in author's files.

31. "Aerial Navigation—Pilcher's Fatal Accident," *English Mechanic and World of Science,* 20 October 1899. Letter from "Aviator."

32. "The Late Mr. Pilcher. (By one who knew him)," *Daily Graphic,* 7 October 1899, p. 9.

33. Clement Henniker Heaton, letter to the author, 20 July 1982.

34. Clarke's original drawing of the triplane components is in the C. H. Bookcase, Envelope 14, RAeS Library. It was reproduced in part in *Aeronautical Classics No. 5. Gliding by Percy S. Pilcher,* published by the ASGB, London, in 1910 (facing page xvii).

35. "Lost without Trace. A Television Treasure Hunt. No. 3 Percy Pilcher's Engine," 6 August 1959, 9.30–10.00 P.M.

36. P. M. Jarrett, "Pilcher's Triplane—A Restoration," *Aerospace,* March 1978, p. 12–19.

37. This Hargrave link seems to have originated in the *Aeronautical Journal* of April 1900, p. 118, where the triplane is described as being "constructed on the principle of the Hargrave soaring kite." Most historians, however, have copied the dramatic but inventive account on page xvii of the "Memoir," which prefaced *Aeronautical Classics No.5. Gliding by Percy S. Pilcher.* Further distortion came as late as 1970, when C. H. Gibbs-Smith stated on page 88 of his book *Aviation* (London, HMSO) that Hargrave's *box kites* provided the inspiration!

38. "Fatal . . . Accident," *Rugby Advertiser,* 7 October 1899.

39. Ibid.; and "The Art of Flying," a letter from "E.F." (the Honorable Everard Feilding) to the editor of *Spectator,* 14 October 1899. Clipping in Chanute's Pilcher scrapbook. Crerar MS. 132.

40. Wilson, "Paper on Pilcher's Gliding Experiments."

41. P. S. Pilcher to A. V. Cave, 23 September 1899, Stanford Hall, Rugby.

42. Statement by Hill in "Fatal . . . Accident," *Rugby Advertiser,* 7 October 1899.
43. "Flying . . . Accident," *Daily Telegraph,* 2 October 1899; "Serious Flying Machine Accident," *Times,* 2 October 1899; "Fatal . . . Accident," *Rugby Advertiser,* 7 October 1899.
44. "The Pilcher Glider," *Flight,* 5 March 1910, p. 151.
45. See n. 28.
46. "The Accident to a Flying Machine," *St. James's Gazette,* 2 October 1899.
47. "The Fatal Accident to Mr. Pilcher," *Aeronautical Journal,* October 1899, p. 88.
48. "Fatal . . . Accident," *Rugby Advertiser,* 7 October 1899; see also n. 28.
49. Some reports suggest that there was only one abortive launch. I have followed the most reliable accounts.
50. "Fatal Accident . . .," *Aeronautical Journal,* October 1899, p. 88.
51. "Accident . . .," *St. James's Gazette,* 2 October 1899.
52. Ibid.
53. "Fatal Accident . . .," *Aeronautical Journal,* October 1899.
54. "Fatal . . . Accident," *Rugby Advertiser,* 7 October 1899.
55. "Mr. Percy S. Pilcher," *Engineering,* 6 October 1899. Clipping in Chanute's Pilcher scrapbook, Crerar MS. 132.
56. *Academy,* 7 October 1899. Clipping in Chanute's Pilcher scrapbook, Crerar MS. 132.
57. "Mr. Percy S. Pilcher," *Engineering,* 6 October 1899.
58. Brompton Cemetery records.
59. "Fatal . . . Accident," *Rugby Advertiser,* 7 October 1899.
60. L. Hargrave to P. S. Pilcher, 4 October 1899, Hargrave Papers, RAeS Library.
61. B. F. S. Baden-Powell to L. Hargrave, 6 October 1899, Hargrave Papers, RAeS Library.
62. Baden-Powell to Chanute, 6 October 1899, Chanute's Pilcher scrapbook, Crerar MS. 132.
63. Hargrave to Baden-Powell, 15 November 1899, Hargrave Papers, RAeS Library.
64. "The Lilienthal and Pilcher Gliders Compared," *Flight,* 1 January 1910, p. 6.
65. P. S. Pilcher, death certificate.
66. "Death of Mr. Pilcher. Fatal Experiments in the Art of Flying," *Daily Mail,* 3 October 1899.
67. "The Flying Machine Fatality. Inquest," *Leicester Daily Post,* 4 October 1899. Clipping in Chanute's Pilcher scrapbook, Crerar MS. 132.
68. Pilcher, *Experiments in Flying Machines,* pp. 8–9.
69. Wilson, paper on Pilcher's Gliding Experiments, p. 6.
70. M. W. McFarland (ed.), *The Papers of Wilbur and Orville Wright* (New York: McGraw-Hill, 1953), vol. 1, pp. 17–18.
71. "Some notes on Percy Pilcher's 'Hawk Glider' a modified type of which was to

have been fitted with a 4½ H.P. engine." Typescript, author and date unknown (possibly Arthur Mee, as the opening two pages of text appear in his book *Enchanted Land* [London: Hodder and Stoughton] first published in 1936.), 11 pp. Copy in author's files made from original in possession of David Forrester, Pilcher's great nephew.

72. M. Hirst, letter to the author, 12 November 1977, including tables and graph.
73. Letter to the author, 1977.
74. W. Wright to O. Chanute, 13 May 1900, in McFarland, *Papers of Wilbur and Orville Wright,* p. 16. W. Wright, "Some Aeronautical Experiments," lecture before the Western Society of Engineers, Chicago, 18 September 1901, in the *Papers,* p. 103, refers to Lilienthal's total flying time.
75. I. R. Liddell, "Percy S. Pilcher," First Pilcher Memorial Lecture, delivered to the Glasgow Branch of the Royal Aeronautical Society 10 February 1956. Typescript of amended second draft in The Royal Museum of Scotland, Edinburgh.
76. Wright, "Some Aeronautical Experiments," p. 102.

Postscript

1. *Aeronautical Journal,* January 1900, p. 95.
2. Ibid.
3. *Aeronautical Journal,* April 1900, inside front cover.
4. Ibid., p. 118.
5. Minute books of the Council of the ASGB, vol. 1, 1866–1909, pp. 191–2, RAeS archives.
6. Ibid., p. 194.
7. H. S. Maxim to E. S. Bruce, 27 September 1900, Maxim letter no. 20, Folder no.4, RAeS Library.
8. ASGB Council Minutes, vol.1, 1866–1909, p. 234.
9. Ibid., p. 239
10. "Two Pioneer Gliders," *Flight,* 10 July 1909, p. 405.
11. "The Lilienthal and Pilcher Gliders Compared," *Flight,* 1 January 1910, pp. 6–8, and 8 January 1910, pp. 19–22.
12. Royal Museum of Scotland records; *Aeronautical Journal,* April 1911, p. 42.
13. ASGB Council Minutes, vol. 2, 1910–18, p. 76.
14. "Loan Exhibition, Science Museum 1912–13," *Aeronautical Journal,* October 1912, p. 221; "Loan Exhibition, Science Museum," *Aeronautical Journal,* April 1913, pp. 105–6; "Aircraft History at South Kensington," *Flight,* 28 December 1912, p. 1229. *Flight,* 1 February 1913, p. 123, reports that the exhibition was extended until "the end of February," but the Hawk must have been removed for display at Olympia in the latter half of February.
15. "What There Will Be to See at Olympia," *Flight,* 8 February 1913, p. 145.

16. "Ghent International Exhibition," *Aeronautical Journal,* April 1913, p. 42; Royal Museum of Scotland records.
17. L. A. Jackson to Lord Braye, 26 March 1962, Stanford Hall.
18. S. Mavor, "Memories No.4. A Pioneer of Flight," *M & C Apprentices' Magazine,* Summer 1934, p. 59.
19. R. C. Gray to E. Tidswell, 21 January 1937. Letter in possession of Mr. David Forrester.
20. R. C. Gray, "Percy Sinclair Pilcher," *College Courant,* vol. 18, no. 15, (Martinmas 1955), p. 42.
21. Original drawings of the triplane components by T. W. K. Clarke, in C.H. Bookcase, Envelope 14, RAeS Library.
22. Director of the Science Museum to J. L. Pritchard, 19 June 1928, Science Museum, London, files.
23. Gray to Tidswell, 21 January 1937.
24. "Lost without Trace, No.3, Percy Pilcher's Engine," BBC script for television program transmitted 6 August 1959, pp. 5–6. Copy in author's files.
25. T. Shreeve to the author, June 1978. In author's files.
26. ASGB Council Minutes books, vol. 1, 1899–1909, p. 199; "General Meeting," *Aeronautical Journal,* April 1902, p. 22.
27. E. Tidswell, "The Work and Experiments of Percy S. Pilcher," *Aeronautical Journal,* July 1909, pp. 87–89.

Appendix C

1. A. G. Wilson, Interview with C. H. Gibbs-Smith, June 1970. Typescript in author's files, pp. 4, 7.
2. "The Wilson and Pilcher Petrol Car," *Automotor Journal,* June 1901, pp. 449–51.
3. "The 10 H.P. Wilson and Pilcher Car," *Autocar,* 14 March 1903, pp. 312–14.
4. "Petrol Cars—Sir W.G. Armstrong Whitworth, and Co., Ltd.," *Autocar,* 20 February 1904, p. 232.
5. Documents covering the liquidation of Wilson and Pilcher Limited are in the company's files in the Public Record Office, reference BT31/7673/54767, London.

Appendix D

1. "General Meeting," *Aeronautical Journal,* January 1912, p. 13.

Appendix E

1. Details from Science Museum records.
2. "Pioneer's Memorial," *Aeroplane,* 14 March 1958, p. 367 (caption); "Full-Scale Replica," *Flight,* 14 March 1958, p. 330 (caption).
3. "Pilcher Glider," *Aeroplane,* 4 April 1958, pp. 466–67; "Percy Pilcher Museum," *Flight,* 4 April 1958, p. 441.
4. "All Strung Up over a Piece of History," *British Aerospace News,* November 1980, p. 10; Mr. Dick Eales in telephone conversation with the author, 4 December 1980.
5. "Sport and Business," *Flight,* 18 December 1959, p. 746; Mr. Walter Neumark in telephone conversation with the author, 6 June 1986.
6. Advertisement, *Sailplane and Gliding,* December 1959.
7. Information supplied by Charles Paton.
8. "Alex Takes TV Series under His Wing," *Sunday Standard,* 30 May 1982; Letter from Alex Gourlay to the author, 12 October 1982.

Index

Boldface numbers refer to illustrations

C

D

E

Q

R

S

T

U

V

W

Y

200 Years of Royal Arch Freemasonry in England 1813-2013

(A Compendium of the Order)